SHANTI PUBLICATIONS

492-E/5-A, Mahaveer Block Street No. 5,
Bhola Nath Nagar, Shahdara, Delhi-110032

RAMAYANA

This Edition:- 2015

Designed by : **Rangoli**

ISBN : 81-7920-270-4

Published By:

SHANTI PUBLICATIONS

492-E/5-A, Mahaveer Block
Street No. 5,
Bhola Nath Nagar, Shahdara
Delhi-110032 (INDIA)
Ph.: 2230 7950
mail at: shantipublications@hotmail.com

CONTENTS

1. ROBBER TURNS SAGE 9
2. FROM SURYAVANSHA TO RAGHUVANSHA 12
3. (BAL KAND) A YAJNA FOR BEGETTING SONS 13
4. THE KHEER IS FRUITFUL 15
5. THE PRINCES TAKE BIRTH 16
6. NAMING CEREMONY OF THE PRINCES 17
7. PERFECTION IN ARCHERY 18
8. THE PRINCES IN THE ASHRAM 19
9. VISHWAMITRA BEFRIENDS VASHISHTHA 20
10. VASHISHTHA THE GREAT GURU 22
11. SUMANTRA IN THE ASHRAM 23
12. DEPARTURE FROM THE ASHRAM 24
13. DEPARTURE TO AYODHYA 25
14. MEETING WITH PARENTS 26
15. A KING TURNS A SAGE 28
16. DEMAND OF VISHWAMITRA 30
17. KILLING OF TARAKA 32
18. IN THE ASHRAM OF VISHWAMITRA 34
19. THE END OF THE OTHER DEMONS 35
20. THE CALL FROM MITHILA 36
21. AHILYA'S SALVATION 37
22. ENTRY INTO MITHILA 39
23. SITA SWAYAMVAR 40
24. LAKSHMANA'S ANGER 42
25. LORD RAMA BREAKS THE BOW 43
26. ENTRY OF PARASHURAMA AT THE SWAYAMVAR 44
27. ANGRY PARASHURAMA 45
28. SITA WEDS RAMA 47
29. WEDDING PROCESSION 48
30. WEDDING CEREMONY 50
31. WELCOME OF THE DAUGHTER-IN-LAW 51
32. (AYODHYA KAND) THE ADVICE OF GURU VASHISHTHA 52
33. THE CALL FROM RAMA 53
34. PREPARATIONS FOR CROWNING CEREMONY 54
35. KAIKEYEE MOVED BY A MAID 55
36. KAIKEYEE IN HER BOUDOIR 57
37. DEMANDS OF KAIKEYEE 59

38. KIND DASHARATHA IMPLORES KAIKEYEE 61

39. KAIKEYEE INTERACTS WITH RAMA 63

40. SENDING RAMA INTO EXILE 65

41. RAMA LEAVES AYODHYA 66

42. SUMANTRA RETURNS TO AYODHYA 67

43. THE DESIRE OF THE BOATMAN 69

44. SAGE BHARDWAJ ADVICES RAMA 71

45. MOURNING OF KING DASHARATHA 72

46. THE STORY OF SHRAVAN KUMAR 73

47. PAINFUL DEATH OF KING DASHARATHA 75

48. BHARATA AND SHATRUGHNA 76

49. CREMATION OF KING DASHARATHA 78

50. REFUSAL OF BHARATA TO BE KING 79

51. MEETING OF RAMA AND BHARATA 81

52. BHARATA RETURNS WITH RAMA'S SLIPPERS 83

53. (ARANYA KAND) VIRADHA MEETS HIS END 84

54. RAMA MEETS SAGE AGASTYA 86

55. RAMA REACHES PANCHVATI 88

56. SHOORPANKHA PROPOSES TO RAMA 89

57. KHARA AND DUSHNA MEET THEIR END 91

58. RAVANA GETS THE NEWS 93

59. RAVANA MEETS MAREECH 94

60. PLAN TO KIDNAP SITA 96

61. A GOLDEN DEAR IN PANCHVATI 98

62. A LINE DRAWN BY LAKSHMANA 100

63. SITA IS KIDNAPPED 102

64. JATAYU FIGHTS AGAINST RAVANA 103

65. RAMA GETS WORRIED 104

66. THE ONE-EYED DEMON 107

67. MEETING WITH SHABRI 109

68. (KISHKINDHA KAND) RAMA AND LAKSHMAN ON RISHYAMOOKA 110

69. A DEVOTEE MEETS HIS ADORED GOD 111

70. RAMA BEFRIENDS SUGREEVA 113
71. BALI IS KILLED 117
72. THE SEARCH FOR SITA 119
73. MEETING A VIRTUOUS WOMAN 121
74. COOPERATION OF A GREAT VULTURE 122
75. THE PRAISE OF HANUMANA 124
76. HANUMANA LEAVES FOR LANKA 127
77. SURSA STOPS HANUMANA 128
78. (SUNDAR KAND) HANUMANA ENTERS LANKA 129
79. HANUMANA MEETS VIBHISHANA 131
80. RAVANA PROPOSES TO SITA 134
81. HANUMANA MEETS SITA 136
82. HANUMANA VERSUS MEGHNADA 140
83. LANKA SET ON FIRE 141
84. HANUMANA RETURNS FROM LANKA 143
85. RAMA GETS WHEREABOUTS OF SITA 145
86. (LANKA KAND) MARCH TO THE SEASHORE 147
87. RAVANA EXILES HIS BROTHER 148
88. RAMA SHELTERS VIBHISHANA 150
89. RAMA PRAYS TO THE SEA 151
90. RAVANA FAILS TO WOO SITA 153
91. SUGREEVA ATTACKS RAVANA 154
92. ANGADA IN THE COURT OF RAVANA 156
93. ATTACK ON LANKA 158
94. FALSE RUMOURS 160
95. GARUDA SAVES LAKSHMANA 161
96. RAVANA JOINS THE WAR 162
97. KUMBHKARANA FORCED TO WAKE UP 164
98. KUMBHKARANA MEETS HIS END 166
99. MAGICAL TRAP OF MEGHNADA 168
100. LAKSHMANA VERSUS MEGHNADA 169
101. LAKSHMANA BECOMES UNCONSCIOUS 171

102. HANUMANA GOES TO
THE HIMALAYAS 173
103. BHARATA ATTACKS
HANUMANA 175
104. THE END OF MEGHNADA 177
105. RAVANA PROCEEDS TO
THE BATTLEFIELD 179
106. SITA UNDERGOES A
FIRE-TEST 183
107. VIBHISHAN BECOMES
KING OF LANKA 185
108. RAMA REACHES
AYODHYA 187
109. (UTTAR KAND) DEVOTION
OF HANUMANA TO RAMA 190
110. RAMA RAJYA—RAMA'S
ADMINISTRATION 192
111. TAUNTING OF A
WASHERMAN 194
112. RAMA ABANDONS SITA 195
113. SITA TAKEN
TO THE FOREST 196
114. SITA AT THE ASHRAM 198
115. LAVA AND KUSHA
ARE BORN 199
116. RAMA ORGANISES
ASHVAMEDHA YAJNA 200

117. LAVA-KUSHA FACE
SHATRUGHNA 202
118. LAKSHMANA VERSUS
LAVA-KUSHA 203
119. BHARATA VERSUS
LAVA-KUSHA 204
120. KUSHA IMPRISONS
HANUMANA 206
121. RAMA MEETS
LAVA-KUSHA 207
122. SITA ENTERS INTO
THE EARTH 209
123. LAVA-KUSHA WELCOMED
AT AYODHYA 211
124. RAMA EXPRESSES HIS
DESIRE 212
125. DHARMRAJ CONSULTS
RAMA 213
126. DEPARTURE OF RAMA
FROM THE EARTH 216
127. RAMA BIDS GOODBYE 217
128. RAMA ENTERS SARYU
RIVER 218
129. PRAISE OF RAMA
BY HANUMANA 219

Preface

Ancient Indian literature has given us two great epics— the Ramayana and the Mahabharata. While the Ramayana emphasises the significance of ideals, the Mahabharata is very close to the present. Both the epics reflect a spectrum of various aspects and realities of life in a delightful manner.

The Ramayana, in Sanskrit language, has been written by the great sage Valmiki. He wrote it in the age of Treta. Thereafter, a medieval saint-poet, Tulsidas, rewrote it in Hindi language. It has immense significance in Hinduism. The Hindus consider it as their holy book and recite its verses daily.

Rama is the hero of Ramayana. He has been taken as the incarnation of Lord Vishnu and his wife Sita as the incarnation of Goddess Laxmi. Rama took birth on the Earth to slay the of demons. He set an example of patience, courage, justice and sacrifice. That is why he has been characterised as 'Maryada Purushottam', a man of exceptional merit. This epic can be related to a typical Indian family. The great affection between the four brothers (Rama, Lakshmana, Bharata and Shatrughna) has been narrated very beautifully and interestingly in this epic. The four brothers did not stray even a little bit from their moral values despite adversities. They followed the path of

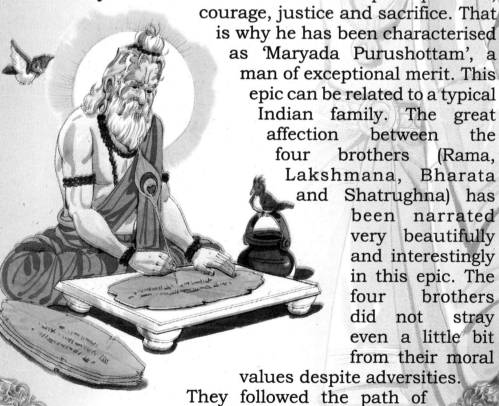

righteous conduct and performed their duties accordingly.

By putting the egoist and sinful king of demons, Ravana, to death, Rama proved that truth always wins over untruth and righteousness always wins over unrighteousness. Although Ravana was a very learned man, his egoism led him to a wrong path. Due to the same egoism he kidnapped Rama's wife Sita. At last, the same egoism caused his death. His moral downfall can be defined by a Sanskrit proverb—'Vinashakale Vipareeta Buddhi'. It means that one's inverted mind symbolises its utter destruction. Thus, we should learn a lesson from his downfall and do everything wisely and contingently.

The Ramayana, in the present perspective, becomes even more important. From this epic let us learn a lesson to make use of love, patience, sacrifice, fraternity, etc. Besides this epic makes us gain courage in the face of dire adversities.

The epic has been translated into other languages as well. Among the Indian languages, it has been translated into Tamil by Kamban, and into Bangla by Kritivasa. It has also been translated into foreign languages.

We present here the stories from the Ramayana in a concise form with the aim to develop good instincts and moral values in our young generation. The language of the stories is simple and lucid.

We hope that the readers will appreciate this faithful rendering of the original text.

ROBBER TURNS SAGE

Long ago, in the mythological period of Treta (as per Hindu mythology, there are four ages of the world—Satya, Treta, Dwapara, and the Kali, the present age), there was a robber named Ratnakar. He used to rob the people in the forest adjacent to his village. After robbing them he used to kill them. People were very afraid of him.

One day, while he was waiting for a prey, he saw Devarishi Narada roaming freely in the jungle. He asked him to hand over whatever he had. But Narada told him, "You are opening the way to hell for yourself by robbing and killing the innocent people." Hearing Narada, Ratnakar said in his defence, "I am doing this to look after my family. It is my duty." In answer to Ratnakar's statement, Narada said, "Are you sure that your family will share the burden of the sin you are committing? Go

9

and ask them. I will wait for you here." Ratnakar thought for a while. Then, he tied Narada to a tree and left for his house. Having reached his house, he asked his parents whether they would share the burden of the sin he is committing to feed them. They refused and said that they never asked him to rob the people. Ratnakar was very surprised. When he put the same question to his wife, she also refused to share the burden of his sin.

Now Ratnakar was disappointed and sad. He thought, 'I have been killing and robbing people only for my family. This way I was opening the way to hell for myself. But my family is not ready to share even the burden of these sins with me.' He came back to the forest and untied Narada.

He fell on the feet of Narada and said, "You have opened my eyes. Kindly guide me to the right path of life."

Narada blessed Ratnakar and said, "I am happy that you have repented on your wrongs. Now chant the name 'Rama' and you will get the salvation of your soul," Saying this, Narada disappeared.

Thereafter, Ratnakar sat under a tree to meditate as advised by the sage, Narada and started chanting the name of Lord Rama. He did this for many years. Even when ants made an anthill around him, he did not move from his place.

The robber Ratnakar later became popular as the great sage Valmiki who wrote *Ramayana*, the great epic in Sanskrit literature.

It is said that the great sage was the contemporary of Lord Rama. Devi Sita lived in his ashram for a long time where Luv and Kush were born.

FROM SURYAVANSHA TO RAGHUVANSHA

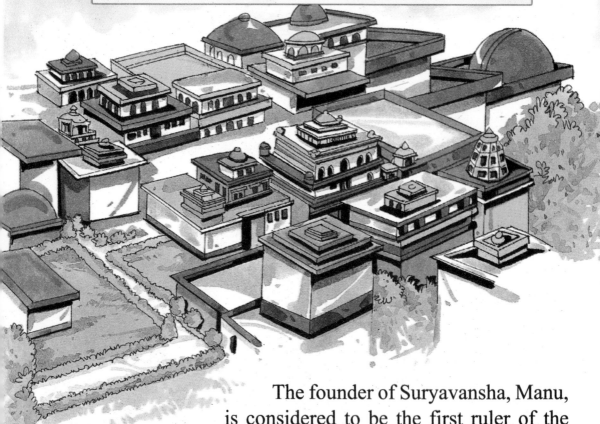

The founder of Suryavansha, Manu, is considered to be the first ruler of the world. His elder son Ikshwaku built a beautiful city called Ayodhya on the banks of the river Saryu. The city was full of all sorts of comforts and riches. King Ikshwaku was very devoted to his duties. His successors were also as devoted to their duties as he was. King Harishchandra, Marajsagar, King Bhagirath, King Dalip, King Ajaa, King Dasharatha and his son Rama were the successors of Ikshwaku.

King Raghu of Suryavansha organised a yajna called Sarvadaan. Thereafter, Suryavansha changed to Raghuvansha.

King Dasharatha was the grandson of Raghu and the son of King Ajaa. He was a kind and religious person. He was devoted to his duties and always took great care of his people. Besides, he was very brave and courageous.

A YAJNA FOR BEGETTING SONS

King Dasharatha had three queens as per the custom prevailing those days. The eldest queen Kaushalya was a religious minded, good natured and kind woman.

The second queen Sumitra was simple and peace loving. The third queen Kaikeyee was very beautiful and intelligent.

King Dasharatha loved all of them equally. Though he had everything, he was not happy because he had no son. To beget a son, King Dasharatha organised a yajna under the guidance of Guru Vashishtha. Pleased with the yajna, Lord Vishnu appeared. The king begged him for a son saying, "Kindly take birth as my son." Lord Vishnu agreed to answer his prayer.

At that moment, a divine being came out of the altar of the yajna with a pot of *kheer* cooked in sweetened milk. He offered it to the king and said, "Give this *kheer* to all the three queens. Soon they will be blessed with sons. Your house will be filled with the

cries of new born babies."

The king took the pot of *kheer* from the divine being and bowed to thank him.

Now, the king was very happy. He was sure of the birth of children in the palace. So he asked Guru Vashishtha to permit him to distribute the *kheer* among the queens. Guru Vashishtha said, "Yes, King Dasharatha, go ahead. May god bless you."

Then the king went to his palace. He divided the *kheer* into three equal shares. First he went to the eldest queen Kaushalya and said, "This *kheer* is offering of the god. Kindly take it." Kaushalya took the *kheer* and ate it.

Then he went to Sumitra and gave her share of the *kheer* to her. Sumitra ate the *kheer* with great love.

Thereafter, the king went to the youngest queen Kaikeyee and gave her share of *kheer*. Kaikeyee ate most of the part of her share of *kheer* but left a little. So, the king went to Sumitra and gave the rest of the share to her. Sumitra ate it again.

This way all the queens ate the *kheer* and awaited good news.

THE KHEER IS FRUITFUL

After consuming the *kheer*, all the queens became pregnant. Hearing this news, King Dasharatha was very happy. All the people of Ayodhya celebrated the news with great pomp and show. All the people were waiting for the princes to come down to the earth. The king and the queens decided to worship the Sun god to express their thanks to Him at the banks of the river Saryu.

First they went to sage Vashishtha to inform him about the pregnancy of the queens. The guru blessed them and said to the king, "Now you should take great care of all the queens. You have to fulfill all their desires and make them happy."

The king and the queens bowed to the sage and came to the bank of the river Saryu. They worshipped the Sun god and expressed their gratitude to Him.

Ever since the queens became pregnant, King Dasharatha took great care of them. He appointed a number of attendants and servants to look after them. The king, the queens as well as the people of Ayodhya were waiting for the birth of the princes very anxiously. Besides them, the gods, the sages and hermits were also waiting for the birth of Lord Vishnu on the earth. In fact, everybody was eager to see the incarnation of Lord Vishnu on the Earth!

At last, the long wait came to an end. On the ninth day of the month of Chaitra, Lord Vishnu incarnated as the son of Kaushalya. As Sumitra took the *kheer* twice she gave birth to two princes and Kaikeyee gave birth to one.

The incarnation of Lord Vishnu on Earth made the gods very happy. Now the sages and hermits were feeling secure. The king, queens and the people of Ayodhya, all were very happy.

King Dasharatha distributed food grains, clothes, ornaments, etc. to the people wholeheartedly.

After thirteen days, the naming ceremony of the princes took place. Guru Vashishtha named the son of Kaushalya as Rama, meaning happiness, peace and prosperity in the world. The son of Kaikeyee was named Bharata, meaning supporter of the world. The sons of Sumitra were named Lakshmana and Shatrughna, meaning the base of the world and the killer of enemies, respectively.

The palace echoed with the cries of the children. Their activities were worth praising. They were the source of recreation for all the people of the palace. This way all the princes passed their time under the care of their mothers and the king.

When the princes reached the age of twelve, King Dasharatha decided to teach them the art of archery. He himself was an expert archer. More precisely, he was able to kill an animal just on hearing its sound.

Once, on account of this art, the king had killed a young man named Shravan Kumar unknowingly. However, he appointed a guru to teach the princes.

Under the guidance of the king and the guru the princes became experts in archery very soon. The king was very happy to see such a progress.

According to tradition, it was now time to send the princes to school. So, King Dasharatha decided to send the boys to the gurukul of Guru Vashishtha for the formal education of the princes. The princes had to give up royal clothes and wear an ordinary dress.

It was necessary for the all round development of the princes that they study with other children. As per rule, all were treated equally in the gurukul.

After their training in weaponry, the princes went to the ashram of Guru Vashishtha to learn Vedas and other shastras. But before the same, a ceremony of wearing the sacred thread 'yajnopaveet' was performed by the guru. It was known as the 'Yajnopaveet Samskar'.

As per convention, the princes had to wear ordinary clothes like others. There was no difference among the pupils in the ashram. The Guru was treated as a god.

The Guru treated all the children as equal despite the difference in their social status. He used to teach religious books, Vedas, social manners and ethical values to the children.

All the princes learnt their lessons well along with the other children from different families.

Guru Vashishtha used to sit for meditation. During meditation he would forget everything in the world. He was a great scholar and a great sage.

Guru Vashishtha was a kind-hearted and generous person. He never showed any sign of revenge even against Vishwamitra who cursed his sons and burnt them to death. Even then he pardoned the latter.

Once Guru Vashishtha was sitting in the moonlight with his wife Arundhati. The moonlight looked so attractive that Arundhati started praising it. She said, "Oh what a beautiful, pure and silver light!"

Having heard it, Vashishtha said, "Oh yes! But it is less attractive and pious than the shining face of the great sage Vishwamitra." This was the greatness of Guru Vashishtha that despite so much of tragedy he had no bad feelings against sage Vishwamitra.

Having heard her husband praising Vishwamitra, Arundhati felt shocked. She said, "Lord! Really your heart is big. You are praising the person who killed your sons. You are great."

"Vishwamitra is worth praising. I am not lying or exaggerating," said Guru Vashishtha in answer to his wife's statement.

Coincidentally, at that time Rishi Vishwamitra was also residing at the ashram of Guru Vashishtha. When he heard the conversation of the couple he realised his mistake and his heart became filled with great devotion for the sage Vashishtha. He rushed to Guru Vashishtha and fell at his feet.

Maharshi hugged him. This way they became friends forever.

VASHISHTHA: THE GREAT GURU

Guru Vashishtha taught his students moral values like truthfulness, religiousness and obedience.

Most of the people of Ayodhya followed the Guru. They did so because of the merits of the Guru. As a result, they were prosperous.

The guru told the princes how to rule and provide for the welfare of the people. The king should be generous, kind and well mannered. Religion and truth should be the base of administration. He should take great care of the people. A king who does injustice to his people goes to hell. Besides all these things, the Guru also taught them about spirituality and humanity.

Ayodhya was prospering due to the blessings of the Guru. The king very often used to come to the Guru for his advice. He helped the king in taking important decisions.

Guru Vashishtha taught many things that are necessary for good administration to the princes.

The princes studied hard at the ashram of Guru Vashishtha. When they completed their education, the guru sent the message to the king to take the princes back to the palace.

As soon as the king got the message, he called his chief minister Sumantra and said, "Sumantra, a message has come from the ashram that the education of the princes is complete. You must go to the ashram with some new clothes for the princes and bring them back to the palace."

Sumantra proceeded to the ashram with a beautiful chariot for the princes. Soon, he reached the ashram.

In the ashram, he bowed to Guru Vashishtha and said, "The king has sent me to take the princes back to the palace." Guru Vashishtha enquired about the welfare of the king and the people of Ayodhya. Thereafter, he called the princess to come quickly and meet Sumantra.

DEPARTURE FROM THE ASHRAM

When Guru Vashishtha called the princes, they came running to him. They touched their guru's feet and said, "Guruji, why have you asked us to come as fast as we could? Is there something very important?"

In answer to the princes' question Guru Vashishtha said, "Your education is now complete. Hence, you have to go back to Ayodhya."

Thus, the princes were told to get ready for the return journey to Ayodhya. Following the order of the guru all the princes started collecting their things. They wore their royal clothes and put the ordinary clothes aside.

Thereafter, they went to Guru Mata and touched her feet. She blessed them all and said goodbye with a heavy heart.

Then, the princes went to Guru Vashishtha and bowed to him. The Guru also blessed them with tearful eyes. He was very sad to see them going after such a long period of time.

While the princes were bidding farewell to their friends and Guru Vashishtha tears rolled down from their eyes. Thereafter, they sat on the chariot and proceeded towards Ayodhya.

When the chariot neared Ayodhya, the princes' hearts filled with happiness. They were eager to meet their parents after such a long time.

The whole town was decorated like a bride. The people were rushing to the road to see the princes who were returning after a long time.

MEETING WITH PARENTS

On the occasion of the return of the princes, not only the town of Ayodhya but also the palace was decorated and illuminated. The princes were welcomed with dance and music.

When the chariot stopped at the gate of the palace the princes rushed to the palace. They were eager to meet their parents. At the gate of the palace queen Kaikeyee was waiting to welcome them.

All the princes bowed to mother Kaikeyee one by one. Rama came forward and touched her feet. Kaikeyee hugged Rama.

Thereafter, Lakshmana, Bharata and Shatrughna touched her feet and got the blessings of their mother Kaikeyee.

It was the first reunion of the princes with their parents after they went to the ashram of Guru Vashishtha for getting education.

After taking the blessings of Kaikeyee, all the princes went to Kaushalya and Sumitra and touched their feet. They blessed them.

This way all the queens met their children.

The reunion of all the children with their mothers was a very touching moment.

Their mothers asked them about the ashram and Guru Vashishtha. They told their mothers about the days spent in the ashram with other children. They narrated that they had to wear ordinary clothes and work with other classmates.

Thereafter, all the princes went to meet their father, King Dasharatha in his room. They all touched their father's feet one by one. The King was very happy to see his grown up children. He was proud of his children who got good education and were able to perform their duties in future. The king blessed his children and hugged them all.

A KING TURNS SAGE

Sage Vishwamitra was initially not a sage. He was born in a royal family. He was a brave and courageous king.

Once, King Vishwamitra came to Guru Vashishtha's ashram to meet him. Sage Vashishtha showed great hospitality and served many delicious dishes to him.

Vishwamitra felt very impressed by the hospitality of the sage. He was also very surprised to see so many precious things in the house of a sage.

So, the king expressed his desire to know the secret of all the luxuries. The sage told him, "It is all due to the gifted cow Kamdhenu. She is a divine cow. And this is the reason of our prosperity."

The king thought that this divine cow should be in his possession. So, he asked the sage to sell the cow to him.

The sage Vashishtha refused to sell the cow Kamdhenu to the king. The refusal made the king very angry and he attacked the ashram of Vashishtha with full force. But with the blessings of Kamdhenu Vashishtha defeated the king.

This defeat changed the life of Vishwamitra. He decided to acquire divine powers like Vashishtha.

Vishwamitra renounced the world. He made his son successor to the throne and went to the forest for penance and meditation. He sat in the same posture for many years. At last, the gods became happy with his penance and meditation and gave him divine powers.

Since then, King Vishwamitra became a sage called Rishi Vishwamitra. He was the sage who led Lord Rama to Janakpuri.

DEMAND OF VISHWAMITRA

One day, when King Dasharatha was discussing something in his court with his ministers, the gate-keeper came and informed him that Rishi Vishwamitra has come to meet him. Hearing this, the king went outside to welcome the sage. The king said, "Gurudev, I am blessed with your kind presence. Please come in. What can I do for you ?"

The sage Vishwamitra said, "Oh King, I have come here to take Rama with me."

"I am unable to understand you," said Dasharatha. Vishwamitra said, "For quite some time two demons Mareech and Subahu are disturbing the peace of my ashram. They destroy the material for pooja-havan and other things. So I want to take Rama with me for protecting the ashram."

He further said, "Rama is brave and courageous. He will certainly kill the demons and protect the ashram.

Having heard the sage, King Dasharatha fell into a dilemma. He was unable to say anything for a moment.

After thinking for a while, he said, "Rama is just a child. He cannot kill the demons. I will go with you to protect your ashram."

Vishwamitra said, "I know you are saying this out of love of Rama, otherwise there is no need to worry. Rama is very wise, brave and courageous. He will certainly kill all the demons around my ashram."

At this moment Guru Vashishtha who was also present there, said to the king, "Vishwamitra is right. You should not worry about the safety of Rama. Send both Rama and Lakshmana with him. They will kill the demons and will come back victorious."

On Guru Vashishtha's insistence King Dasharatha agreed to send both the sons Rama and Lakshmana with Rishi Vishwamitra.

KILLING OF TARAKA

After taking the permission of their parents and guru, Rama and Lakshmana went to the forest of Dandak with the sage, Vishwamitra. The forest was echoing with the sounds made by various animals and roaring of wild animals.

Sage Vishwamitra warned both Rama and Lakshmana to be beware of the demoness Taraka who lived in that area. "She keeps an eye on every movement of the forest and kills the innocent. She has the strength of a thousand elephants. She is very proud of herself and does not care for any one. All the forest dwellers are afraid of her. Her atrocities are increasing day by day. You have to kill her," he said.

Hearing the sage, Rama smiled. He pulled the string of his bow. It produced a sharp sound. Having heard that sound, all the

birds flew away and the animals rushed to their home. The sound of the string was also heard by the demoness Taraka. She ran in the direction of the sound and immediately reached Rama and Lakshmana. She was very big and dark. Her teeth and nails were very sharp and she was very fearsome too.

As Taraka moved towards Rama, the latter aimed an arrow at her. The arrow hit and killed her instantly. She fell on the ground with a thud. Having seen the mighty Taraka lying dead on the ground, the gods from the sky showered flowers on Rama.

After the fall of Taraka, sage Viswamitra blessed Rama and said, "By killing Taraka you have shown an extraordinary courage. But the troubles of the people of Dandakvan still remain. Now you must get prepared to face Mareech and Subahu. After receiving the news of Taraka they will become more furious and will try to attack you with all their power. So beware of them."

Then, the sage came to his ashram along with Rama and Lakshmana. When the people heard that Rama had killed Taraka, they danced with joy and welcomed the princes.

Rama said to Vishwamitra, "Gurudev, please, start your religious ceremonies from tomorrow onwards. We both will keep an eye on the demons." All the people of the ashram slept well without fear that night.

Next morning the prayers and chanting of hymns and mantras echoed in the ashram.

THE END OF THE OTHER DEMONS

When Vishwamitra was performing a yajna with other members of his ashram, he heard some disturbing noises coming from the sky. To find out their source, Rama and Lakshmana looked towards the sky and caught sight of Mareech and Subahu.

The two demons, Mareech and Subahu were throwing meat and blood from the sky. It disturbed the sacred yajna. Having seen this, Rama aimed the Manavastra towards them. Though this weapon injured Mareech and threw him several thousand miles away into the sea, it did not kill him. Then, Rama killed Subhau with Agneyastra. After doing this, Rama and Lakshmana killed both the demons.

Having seen such a display of courage, Vishwamitra and the members of his ashram blessed Rama and Lakshmana.

Janaka was the king of Mithila. He had a daughter named Sita. When Sita became old enough to be married the king decided to organise a Swayamvar for her.

He invited the kings and princes of all the states to take part in this ceremony. He also invited the sage Vishwamitra to this ceremony. Having received the invitation, Vishwamitra said to Rama and Lakshmana, "Tomorrow we will proceed towards Mithila. The king of Mithila has invited us to the Swayamvar of his daughter Sita. I want you to take part in it. In the ceremony, you will see an old bow of Lord Shiva. The challenge of the Swayamvar is to string the bow. Whosoever does this job will get Sita as his wife."

Both the princes expressed their willingness to go there. The sage, Vishwamitra knew that Rama is the incarnation of Lord Vishnu and Sita is actually the incarnation of Lakshmi. So, he predicted that the time of their final meeting had arrived.

Next day, Vishwamitra, Rama and Lakshmana proceeded towards Mithila. On the way to Mithila, they saw an empty hut. There was peace and quiet all around the hut. Then, they saw a stone in the form of a woman. Having seen it, Rama felt surprised and asked, "Gurudev! Why is this hut empty? Who lives here? And what's this stone meant for?"

In reply to Rama's question, Vishwamitra said, "This hut belongs to the sage Gautama. He used to live here with his wife Ahilya. Ahilya was a very beautiful woman. Once Lord Indra saw Ahilya and became mesmerised by her beauty.

"One day, when the sage was not at home, he took advantage of the situation and transformed himself into the image of Gautama. Ahilya was unable to recognise Lord Indra as he was in the form of her husband. So, she did not object to closeness with him.

After committing such a crime, Indra felt guilty and thought to leave that place. But before he could do so, the sage came back.

Having seen Indra leaving his house in a hurry, he became suspicious. With the help of his divine powers he found out the reason behind it. He became angry and cursed Indra that he will become impotent. Then, he entered the hut and cursed his wife, "You will become a stone. After becoming stone, no one will be able to see your beauty. Only when Lord Rama will touch you with his foot you will become a woman again."

Having heard this, Lord Rama touched the stone with his foot and Ahilya came back to her original form. She thanked him.

To show her gratitude, Ahilya touched Lord Rama's feet and thanked him.

Having completed their journey, Rama, Lakshmana and Vishwamitra reached Mithila. King Janaka welcomed them.

King Janaka possessed qualities of both a king and a sage. During meditation he used to forget his physical self because of which he was also known by the name 'Videh'.

When King Janaka saw Maharshi Vishwamitra with two beautiful princes he became curious to know about them. So he started enquiring about the princes.

Vishwamitra said, "Oh King! These two princes are sons of King Dasharatha of Ayodhya. It is my good fortune that they are accompanying me. They are the masters of many skills and courage. It is because of their valour that now I am able to perform my yajnas without the fear of demons like Mareech and Subahu." Saying this, he introduced Rama and Lakshmana to King Janaka who warmly welcomed them and offered a seat.

In the Swayamvar, kings and princes from far and remote areas were also present. Everybody wanted to win the hand of Sita in marriage. Even the king of Lanka, Ravana, was present there.

After some time, Sita entered the room with a garland in her hands. The divine beauty of Sita mesmerised everyone present in the entire hall.

With the entry of Sita, the Swayamvar started.

Many brave kings belonging to different kingdoms tried their physical might on the bow of Lord Shiva, but far from lifting it, they could not even budge the bow an inch from its place. They failed badly in their attempts to lift the bow of Lord Shiva.

Even the mighty Ravana was unable to lift the bow.

Having seen all this, the king of Mithila, Janaka became sad and disappointed. He said, "If I had known that this earth has become devoid of the brave, I wouldn't have asked anyone to

come here and take part in the Swayamvar of my daughter Sita. Now I do not want to displease or disrespect anybody who thinks of himself to be mighty or valorous. So, please, return to your respective kingdoms and forget about marrying Sita."

All the kings and princes present in the Swayamvar were feeling embarrassed to hear such bitter comments of Janaka except Lakshmana.

Lakshmana was unable to see that the comments of King Janaka were actually the outpourings of a sad and disappointed father. He took it as a insult of Raghuvansha and became angry.

LAKSHMANA'S ANGER

Having heard the insulting words of King Janaka, Lakshmana lost his temper. He stood up from his seat and said, "Oh King! Nobody dares to speak such offensive words in the presence of the progeny of Raghu dynasty. If my brother Lord Rama permits, I can not only tie the bowstring of this bow but can also run several miles while carrying it in my hands. This bow is nothing. I can even carry the whole universe in my hands like a ball."

Having seen Lakshmana in such an angry mood, Lord Rama tried to pacify him by saying, "Brother! Don't be so angry. Anger is not a good thing. Now take a seat beside me."

"Brother Rama! I cannot ignore your orders that is why I won't break this bow. Moreover, it will be against the rules. You are my elder brother so you should accomplish this task," said Lakshmana. After saying so, he came back to his seat. Having heard the words of Lakshmana, Sita became happy. She looked towards Rama with eyes full of hope while at the same time praying to Goddess Parvati in her heart.

LORD RAMA BREAKS THE BOW

Taking it to be an opportune time, Vishwamitra said, "O Rama, make a name for Raghuvansha by tying the string of Lord Shiva's bow. And relieve King Janaka from his mental agony."

Rama touched the feet of the sage Vishwamitra and said, "Gurudev, I will do as you wish." After taking the permission of the sage, Rama went up to the bow of Lord Shiva. All the people present in the assembly were watching this with bated breath. Nobody knew what was in the womb of future.

Lord Rama lifted the bow effortlessly. As soon as he tried to tie its bowstring, it broke into two parts. The sound it produced shook the earth. Having seen this, all the members of the assembly became surprised while the face of King Janaka started glowing with happiness.

The breaking of the bow of Lord Shiva produced a loud deafening sound whose resonance reverberated in all the directions. It disturbed Parashurama's meditation. He became angry and rushed to the palace with a bow in one hand and axe in the other. Seeing him in such an angry mood, all the members of the assembly including King Janaka himself got terribly frightened. Everyone knew about his ever wrathful nature. When Parashurama saw the broken bow of Lord Shiva lying there in Swayamvar hall, he asked King Janaka angrily, "O King! Tell me, who dared to break the bow of Lord Shiva. Bring him before me or I will turn your kingdom upside down."

Having heard the words of Parashurama, Janaka became so frightened that he could not utter anything. He knew that Parashurama hated Kshatriyas because once a Kshatriya king killed his father. To take revenge he erased Kshatriyas from the face of the earth twenty one times.

Having seen Parashurama in such a foul mood, Rama tried to pacify him by saying, "O Great Sage! Whosoever has broken the bow of Lord Shiva is your humble servant. Just order what you want and he will obey your orders."

Parashurama said, "Whosoever has broken the bow of Lord Shiva is not my servant, he is my enemy. I won't leave him alive. Just tell me who is it."

At this, Lakshmana stood up from his seat and said, "O Great Sage! You are getting angry without any reason. I have broken several bows during my childhood days, but you never got angry with me. What's so special about this bow that you..."

While Lakshmana was about to complete his statement Parashurama interrupted. He said, boiling with anger, "You fool! How dare you compare the world famous bow of Lord Shiva with an ordinary one. Do you want to die?"

When Rama saw that the altercation between Lakshmana and

Parashurama was rising to a higher degree, he intercepted and said to Lakshmana, "Brother! Don't get angry. I will clear away the doubts of the sage Parashurama."

Then, Rama said to Parashurama, "I am Rama, the son of the King Dasharatha of Ayodhya. I have broken this bow accidently while tying its bowstring."

Parashurama said, "O the son of Dasharatha! I will consider you to be powerful only if you succeed in tying the bowstring of my bow. This bow belongs to Lord Vishnu. He gave it to my father. Only he could tie the bowstring of this bow. If you fail to tie its bowstring, you will have to fight with me." Rama took his bow and tied its bowstring. Then, Lord Rama said, "What should I do with you now? Should I take your divine powers?" Now, Parashurama became aware that Rama is the incarnation of Lord Vishnu. So, Parashurama made an apology to Rama.

Having seen Rama's bravery and humility, the sage Parashurama became impressed with him. Leaving Mithila behind he proceeded to the Mahendra mountain for meditation.

In the meanwhile, the time to perform the marriage ceremony of Rama and Sita had finally arrived. Carrying the garland in her hands princess Sita with her friends stood in front of Rama.

Having seen the divine glow on Lord Rama's face, Sita became transfixed. She was unable to move from her place. Seeing this, one of her friends said, "Sita, go ahead and take Rama as your husband." Then, Sita placed a garland around Rama.

Having seen his beloved daughter Sita being married to the brave prince Rama, Janaka was very happy. After the completion of the Swayamvar, King Janaka sent the message to King Dasharatha. The messenger, on reaching Ayodhya, informed King Dasharatha that Rama had married Sita, the princess of Mithila, after breaking the bow of Lord Shiva. On hearing about the bravery of his son, Dasharatha became filled with pride. The three queens of Dasharatha were also very happy. All of them started making preparations for going to Mithila.

Having made all the preparations, King Dasharatha with his queens finally proceeded to Mithila for Rama and Sita's marriage ceremony. A huge procession followed them. In addition to the relatives and friends, a large number of common peasants of Ayodhya were also accompanying them. Everybody was eager to see their favourite prince getting married. The sages who were invited to the wedding ceremonies, were also sitting in the chariots. The great pomp and gaiety of the procession was worth seeing. Everybody was happy.

On the outskirts of Mithila, King Janaka was waiting to receive them. Having seen King Dasharatha accompanied by a huge procession, he extended a hearty welcome to them. Having received such a warm welcome King Dasharatha and all the people became happy. Thereafter, they entered Mithila carrying gems and beautiful clothes. When peasants of Mithila saw Lord Rama they became mesmerised by his stately and grand appearance. They began looking at him with unblinking eyes. The whole atmosphere of Mithila was full of happiness.

In his palace, King Janaka had made grand arrangements for the marriage ceremony of Rama and Sita.

King Janaka had a younger brother named Kushadhwaja. Kushadhwaja had two daughters named Mandavi and Shrutikeerti. They too were old enough to get married. Urmila was the sister of Sita.

On the advice of the sage Vishwamitra and guru Vashishtha marriage of Urmila with Lakshmana, Mandavi with Bharata and Shrutikeerti with Shatrughna also took place under the same roof with great pomp and show.

WELCOME OF DAUGHTERS-IN-LAW

After the completion of the marriage ceremonies, Vishwamitra proceeded towards the Himalayas for meditation. Being happy with the marriage of his four sons, King Dasharatha gifted four lakh cows to the brahmins of Mithila. At the time of Vidaai, the brides approached their mothers and asked for their blessing. The mothers of the newly married brides taught their daughters how to fulfil their duties towards their husbands. They also told them to serve their parents-in-law with devotion. King Janaka and his brother also gave their daughters precious gems and silk clothes as gifts.

Thereafter, King Dasharatha said goodbye to Janaka and started his return journey to Ayodhya with his sons, daughters-in-law and the procession.

When they reached the main entrance of Ayodhya, the queens Kaushalya, Sumitra and Kaikeyee welcomed their sons and daughters-in-law in the traditional way and gave their blessing for a happy married life.

THE ADVICE OF GURU VASHISHTHA

The newly-wedded princes started leading their lives in conjugal bliss. The understanding between Sita and Rama was worth praising. For twelve years their domestic lives remained free of all troubles.

In the meantime, the maternal uncle of Bharata and Shatrughna visited Ayodhya. When he was returning home, Bharata and Shatrughna accompanied him.

King Dasharatha was getting old day by day. Having seen this, Guru Vashishtha advised him to declare Rama the crown prince of Ayodhya. King Dasharatha also wanted to do this. So, he expressed his consent to the idea.

Soon, King Dasharatha called a meeting of all his ministers to discuss this topic.

When the ministers of King Dasharatha came to know about his decision, they became happy. They not only showed their agreement but also praised the king for his wisdom.

Having discussed the matter with Guru Vashishtha and his ministers, King Dasharatha decided to make Rama the crown prince of Ayodhya. Then, King Dasharatha asked his chief minister Sumantra to bring the prince Rama in the assembly.

Having received the orders, Rama presented himself at the assembly and bowed in front of his father. King Dasharatha blessed him and said, "Ram! I am getting old. I have completed all my duties as a king and as a father. Now I want you to take the responsibility of the kingdom. The whole assembly has voted in your favour. Tomorrow we will perform your crowning ceremony." He further added, "You have attained accomplishments in every respect by now and the people of Ayodhya love you. Thus, you have all the qualities a king needs. I believe that you will become a great king." Lord Rama accepted the decision of his father.

PREPARATIONS FOR THE CROWNING CEREMONY

In the main hall of the palace, the preparations for the crowning ceremony of Lord Rama were taking place. King Dasharatha sent a message to Guru Vashishtha requesting him to come to the palace. Having received the message, Guru Vashishtha proceeded to the palace. When he reached the palace, King Dasharatha bowed to him and said, "Gurudev! You know that before the crowning ceremony Rama and Sita have to fast, but they don't know anything about it. So, I am requesting you to teach them how fasting should be done."

"Alright, King Dasharatha! I will tell Rama about the rules of fasting." After saying this he entered Rama's room.

Having seen him, Rama asked him to take a seat and said, "Gurudev! Tell me, what I can do for you."

In reply to Rama's question, Guru Vashishtha said, "Rama, tomorrow is your crowning ceremony. Before that you and your wife have to fast. I will tell you some mantras. Chant these mantras and sleep on the floor."

Rama followed the instructions of the guru well.

KAIKEYEE MOVED BY A MAID

When the news of the crowning ceremony of Rama reached Queen Kaikeyee's favourite maid Manthara, she became upset. She approached the queen and said, "Queen Kaikeyee! Where are you? I heard that Rama is about to become the king."

"That's good news. I am feeling very happy to hear that my son Rama is about to become the king. You should be given a present for breaking the news for me." Having said so, Kaikeyee removed her diamond necklace and offered it to Manthara.

But the latter was not ready to accept her defeat. So, she threw the necklace on the floor and said to the queen, "O my simple Queen! You are so innocent that you are celebrating Rama's coronation ceremony without knowing its consequences. If Rama becomes a king, Queen Kaushalaya will be the Queen Mother while your son Bharata will remain a mere servant of Rama."

The bitter words of Manthara succeeded in hitting the target. Having heard these words, Kaikeyee got lost in thoughts. After thinking for some time, she said to the maid, "Manthara! You know that Rama is the eldest among all the brothers and the crown rightfully belongs to him. So, tell me, how can I change this tradition?"

In reply to the queen's question Manthara said, "Queen! Don't be worried. I have a solution to this problem. Don't you remember the two boons the king once promised to give you? Now is the golden opportunity to ask for those boons."

"Manthara, I don't understand what you are trying to say?" said the queen curiously.

Manthara explained by saying, "Queen! Demand the crowning of Bharata in the first and banishment of Rama to the forest for fourteen years in the second boon." Under the deceptive influence of Manthara, Kaikeyee agreed to do so.

KAIKEYEE IN HER BOUDOIR

After taking the advice of Manthara, Kaikeyee retreated to her boudoir. To show her dissatisfaction she took off her silk clothes and donned the most indifferent clothes. She also took off her jewellery and refused to comb her hair. She also started crying aloud.

According to the plan, Manthara sent a maid to the king. She instructed her to tell the king to meet Queen Kaikeyee quickly. The maid approached the king and said, "Sire! Queen Kaikeyee has asked you to meet her immediately."

Having received the message, King Dasharatha proceeded to the room of Kaikeyee. While on the way to the queen's room, the king was thinking, 'What could be so important that Kaikeyee has asked me to come immediately.'

When he reached Kaikeyee's room, he saw that she was not there. So he called a maid and asked the whereabouts of the queen. The maid informed him that the queen had retreated to her boudoir. So, he went to meet her in the boudoir itself. When he saw the queen crying aloud in her boudoir, he became worried and said, "O Queen! What's the matter? Why are you crying when the whole palace is making preparations for the coronation of Rama? Why have you donned these simple and cheap clothes in such a big function? Would you tell me why you are doing all this?"

King Dasharatha asked the queen these questions several times. But she never answered them. Then, he tried to reach out his hand to touch her but the latter pushed it aside and turned her head.

Having seen this, King Dasharatha became irritated and said, "Queen! Tell me, what do you want? I promise, I will fulfill all your demands."

DEMANDS OF KAIKEYEE

After so much insistence, Kaikeyee uttered, "You must have remembered the incidence in the battlefield when you had been wounded. I took your chariot to a safe place and took out the arrows from your body and saved your life. After regaining consciousness, you were very happy with me and promised me a boon of my choice.

"At that time I told you that I do not want any boon from you. But you promised two boons at any time. Dear King, do you remember your promise?"

Having listened to Kaikyee, Dasharatha said, "I do remember promises and also remember the time when you saved my life. If you want, you can ask for those two boons right now. I promise, whatever you ask will be yours."

Having heard this,
Kaikeyee felt happy but she
controlled her feelings. After thinking for some time, she said,
"In the first boon, I demand the throne for my son Bharata, and
in the second boon, I demand exile of Rama for fourteen years."

Having heard Kaikeyee's demands, King Dasharatha was
stunned. He felt the ground below his feet is slipping. When he
realised that fulfilling these boons meant separation from his
beloved son Rama, he started weeping loudly. Despite seeing
the pathetic condition of the king, Kaikeyee did not change her
stand. Then, the king fell on the feet of Kaikeyee and said, "I can
live without food and water but not without Rama. Rama is my
life. Please do not snatch him from me. You can ask for any
other thing. I will fulfill all of your demands. If Rama goes out, I
will not be able to live any more in the world." But Kaikeyee
remained stuck to both her demands.

King Dasharatha continued to implore Kaikeyee but she remained unmoved. He said, "Dear, you know, Rama is very simple and pure hearted. How can I send him to the forest full of demons and wild animals? You are a mother and it is strange that you are acting so cruelly. You are not taking my old age into consideration. I will not be able to tolerate the separation from Rama. Hence, I again request you to please change your mind." But Kaikeyee spoke to him in a very rude tone, "Oh

King! I heard that the Raghuvanshis are known for keeping their promises at any cost. They even sacrifice their life for the sake of their word. But now I feel that it is just a proverb. But remember that I am also firm in my demands and if you fail to fulfil them, I will commit suicide. So, once again I repeat my demands that you give the throne to my son Bharata and fourteen years' exile to Rama."

By now Dasharatha had realised that the

queen will not change her demands. But the separation from his beloved son was unthinkable for him. He was totally helpless. So, as a last effort he advised the queen, "Dear, forget your obstinacy, otherwise there would be destruction and your name will be written in black letters in the history of Raghuvansha. It is time to change your mind."

But Kaikeyee remained stubborn. She did not move at all from her stand. On the other hand, the preparation for the coronation of Rama was in full swing. Guru Vashishtha was already there. He asked the chief minister Sumantra to bring the king to the function so that the auspicious time may not pass.

As soon as Sumantra reached the palace Kaikeyee said, "Please, send Rama here as the king wants to meet him."

Rama was getting ready for the coronation. As soon as he got the message from Sumantra, he proceeded to meet the king.

When Rama reached the king he was surprised to see the pathetic condition of his father.

He bowed to the king and asked mother Kaikeyee with folded hands, "Is father alright? Why is he looking so sad?"

Kaikeyee said, "Your father is alright but a little disturbed. The reason is that last night he asked me to demand two boons. Accordingly, I demanded two boons then and there. Since then he seems to be perturbed."

Kaikeyee further said, "These boons were pending since I saved the life of your father in the battlefield and he promised to give me two boons of my choice any time."

Rama asked, "May I know what are those two promises?" Kaikeyee replied, "I asked for the throne of Ayodhya for my son Bharata as the first boon and in the second boon, I asked for an

exile for you for fourteen years in the forest.

Rama assured Kaikeyee, "Please, do not worry. The two promises will be executed word by word."

Having heard the words of Rama, Kaikeyee became very happy and said, "I was expecting this from you."

Rama touched the feet of Kaikeyee and after taking her blessings came out of the palace.

Lakshmana who was hearing the conversation between mother Kaikeyee and his elder brother Rama followed the latter silently.

Having returned from Kaikeyee's room Rama first went to take the blessings of mother Kaushalya and then of mother Sumitra.

SENDING RAMA INTO EXILE

Rama went to mother Kaushalya and told her all. She became very sad and said, "I will not allow you to go into exile."

Rama replied, "It is the duty of every son to obey his parents. Bless me so that I can fulfill my responsibility."

When Sita and Lakshmana found out that Rama was going into exile for fourteen years, they also decided to go with him. All the three donned saffron coloured clothes instead of silks.

Thereafter, all the three went to the king and sought his blessings. Then they went to the mothers Kaushalya and Sumitra who said goodbye to them with tears in their eyes.

Accompanied by Sumantra, they all sat on a chariot and proceeded to the forest. The people of Ayodhya were weeping over the news of the exile. Even the birds and animals were very sad on the departure of Rama because he loved them all.

While Rama, accompanied by Lakshmana and Sita, was leaving Ayodhya to go into exile the people of the city were following the trio. When they reached the bank of the river Tamsa, Lakshmana prepared a bed of grass for Rama and Sita. He himself stood as a guard for the whole night.

Just before dawn, Rama said to Sumantra, "The people are sleeping now. They will not allow us to go ahead on awakening. Hence, take us quickly across the river."

Hearing this, Sumantra bowed to Rama and proceeded to prepare the chariot. Soon, he took Rama, Lakshmana and Sita to the forest. When the people woke up in the morning and found Rama already gone, they all became sad and returned to their homes with a heavy heart.

SUMANTRA RETURNS TO AYODHYA

Sumantra drove the chariot to the forest and soon reached the bank of Ganga. Rama decided to stay there overnight.

There was a village of tribals near the Ganga. The head of the village named Guhu was a devotee of Rama.

When he found out that Rama was staying in his village, he went there and bowed to him. Then, he said, "Kindly accept our request and stay here for the whole period of the exile. It would make my village pious and I will be blessed with your presence."

Hearing the request of Guhu, Rama said, "Sorry, we have been asked to live in the forest and have to live like nomads. We cannot stay and lead a life in luxury and comfort. The period of fourteen years has to be spent at different places. We will stay

here only for tonight and tomorrow morning we will proceed to another place. At this Guhu returned to his village with a heavy heart.

Next day, in the morning, Rama said to Sumantra, "Now, please, go back to Ayodhya and look after our respected father. His health was not good when we left home. It is your duty now to serve him well."

At this, Sumantra became very sad and started weeping. Rama consoled him and said, "You are our family friend. My father is in shock at this time. You can console him and nurse him well. Tell the people that we are happy in the forest. Tell my father to forget the incident and look after the welfare of the people. I know that you are also sad by this incident. So, I advise you to be tolerant and treat this as part of life. So, get back to Ayodhya as soon as possible."

Hearing Rama, Sumantra became silent and stopped weeping. Thereafter, following the order of Rama, he asked the charioteer to take the chariot back towards Ayodhya.

THE DESIRE OF THE BOATMAN

After the departure of Sumantra, Rama, Sita and Lakshmana reached the bank of the river Ganga. They asked a number of boatmen to take them across the river but none was ready to do so. Then Lord Rama asked one of the boatmen the reason for their refusal.

The boatman said, "I know that you are a magician. When you touch a thing it becomes alive. I have also heard that once, when you touched a stone with your feet, it immediately turned to a woman. That is why I am afraid that if you touch my boat it will turn into a woman. Then, how will I feed my family without the boat? But if you still want to go across the river, kindly allow me to wash your feet with the holy water of Ganga."

Having heard this, the embodiment of kindness, Lord Rama smiled and said, "If you want to wash my feet for your satisfaction, you can do so. But if you think that there is magic in the dust of my feet, I assure you that there is no magic in it."

Having received the permission of Rama, the boatman became very happy. He rushed to the river Ganga and brought the water

to wash the feet of Lord Rama. Then, he distributed the holy water among his family members.

Thereafter, he took Rama, Sita and Lakshmana across the river. After crossing the river, Sita thought that the boatman should be given something for his service. So, she offered him her ring as the fare for crossing the river. But the boatman stood with folded hands before her and said, "You have made my boat sacred by sitting in it. All my sins are washed away. I am very lucky that you have given me an opportunity to serve you. Hence, I will not take the fare." Seeing such affection of the boatman Lord Rama blessed him. Thereafter, Rama took a bath in the river and then worshipped Lord Shiva.

Sita also took bath and then prayed to the Ganga, "We are very lucky that you have given us an opportunity to bathe in your holy water. All our sins are washed away. May god help us to get another chance to take a bath in your holy water!"

Having heard the prayer of Sita, the goddess Ganga appeared before her and said, "Dear daughter, my blessing is with you. Soon, your fourteen years of exile will be over and you will come back home happily" saying this, the goddess disappeared.

Having received the blessings of the goddess Ganga, the trio went to the forest. As there was danger in the forest, Rama said to Lakshmana, "Keep Sita in the middle. I will walk ahead of Sita and you behind her. This way Sita will be safe in the jungle."

Having heard Rama, Lakshmana took the position behind Sita while Rama was in the front . Next day, they reached the ashram of the sage Bhardwaj. All the three bowed to him. Then they asked for a suitable place to live.

Sage Bhardwaj advised them to live in Chitrakoot. He said, "The place is safe and there is peace all around." Rama accepted the advice and proceeded to Chitrakoot.

In Ayodhya, King Dasharatha was expecting the return of Rama. He was hoping that Sumantra would make Rama come back to Ayodhya. But, on the contrary, Sumantra returned alone. Seeing Sumantra alone Dasharatha lost all hope. He was feeling as if everything had gone. He asked Sumantra, "Where are Rama, Lakshmana and Sita? If they cannot come here, take me there to them." Kaushalya also said, "Why did you leave Rama in the forest which is full of wild animals and demons? Take me there. I cannot live without him."

The separation from his beloved son Rama affected the health of King Dasharatha badly. His condition started becoming worse and worse. One day, all of a sudden, he remembered an incident of his youth and said lamenting, "It is said that every man gets the punishment for its sins. I remember that once I killed a young man by mistake and his parents cursed me before death that I would also die of separation from my son. Today, I am being punished for the same act of sin."

THE STORY OF SHRAVAN KUMAR

On Kaushalya's insistence, King Dasharatha started narrating the story of his youth. He said, "Kaushalya! You know that I am able to shoot at any sound. One day, when I was young, I went to the forest for hunting. When I was returning home, while crossing the river Saryu to reach the palace, I heard the gurgle of water. I thought it to be some elephant drinking water from the river. Without a second thought, I took an arrow and shot in the direction of the sound. But I was surprised when instead of hearing the voice of an elephant, I heard the painful cry of a human being. I ran towards the same. When I reached there, I saw a young man pierced by my arrow."

"The young man named Shravan Kumar, said crying in pain, 'who are you and why have you shot me? Now my death is due. Nobody can change that. But, if you have any remorse for this dreadful act, do one thing for me. I came here to take water for my parents who are blind and thirsty. Please, go to them and give them some water to drink. But do not tell about my death, otherwise they will not take any water.'

"Saying this he died in my lap. When I reached the blind parents with water they said, 'Why have you come so late? We are very thirsty. Give us the water.' I gave them the water but remained silent. Because of my silence they became restless and asked again, 'Why are you not speaking?' Seeing their restlessness and uneasiness I narrated the incident with a heavy heart.

"Hearing that their son was dead, they lamented and cursed me, 'As we are dying due to separation from our son so will you.'

"Saying this, the parents died and I returned to the palace."

PAINFUL DEATH OF KING DASHARATHA

When she heard about the incident, Kaushalya was stunned. She had no words to console the king. However, Dasharatha continued to lament, "Kaushalya, my end is very near. The messengers of Yama (god of death) are here. Will my Rama save me from the trap of these messengers?"

For six days King Dasharatha lamented and died on the seventh day. All the people of Ayodhya became sad.

Bharata and Shatrughna had not yet returned from the house of their maternal uncle. So, Guru Vashishtha sent a messenger to them but warned him not to disclose about the death of Dasharatha. "They will come to know it when they come here," he said.

The messenger immediately proceeded to inform the princes. Guru Vashishtha made arrangements for the preservation of the body of the king till the return of Bharata and Shatrughna.

The dead body was preserved till then by the use of medicines.

BHARATA AND SHATRUGHNA RETURN HOME

The messenger reached Kaikeyee Desh and delivered the message of Guru Vashishtha. Hearing the order of the guru, both the princes, Bharata and Shatrughna got ready for the journey back home. They took the permission of their maternal uncle and proceeded towards Ayodhya. On the eighth day, when they reached Ayodhya and saw gloomy the atmosphere there, they were surprised. Seeing Ayodhya in such a state Bharata said to Shatrughna, "It doesn't look the same as when we left it. Ayodhya looks gloomy and abandoned. What's happened here?" To find out the reason behind the state of Ayodhya they ran to the palace. First, they went to their father's room but did not find him there. Then, they went to Kaikeyee's room. She was very happy to see them and both of them touched the feet of their mother. Then they asked about their father.

Kaikeyee said, "Your father led a life of an ideal king. But now he has gone to his eternal home. So, we should not lament for him."

Having heard the news of Dasharatha's death, both the princes started weeping bitterly. Then, they asked about Rama, Lakshmana and Sita. Kaikeyee told them everything from the beginning to the end. She also told Bharata how she was able to get the throne for him.

Hearing this, Bharata got annoyed and spoke in an agitated voice, "You are the killer of my father. You have conspired to send my brother and Mata Sita to the forest. From now on I won't address you as my mother. I have no relation with you from now onwards."

When Shatrughna found out that Manthara played an important part in the conspiracy, he did not spare her either.

The untimely death of King Dasharatha made Bharata very sad. Guru Vashishtha consoled him, "My son Bharata, have patience. We know it is very difficult to forget this tragedy but you have to work with patience. You know that Rama is not here. So, you have to perform the last rites of your father."

As per the directions of the guru, Bharata made preparations for the cremation of his father. The funeral pyre was prepared of sandal wood at the bank of the river Saryu. The dead body was kept on the pyre.

With the recitation of verses from Vedas, Bharata did the cremation of his father Dasharatha. Thereafter, they all took bath in the Saryu and offered libation to the soul. For the salvation of his father's soul he also gave a lot of things to the brahmins and the poor.

After the death of Dasharatha, thirteen days were observed as the mourning days. On the fourteenth day, Guru Vashishtha called the meeting of ministers. In the meeting, it was decided that Bharata should be asked to sit on the throne.

Hence, Guru Vashishtha asked Bharata to sit on the throne and perform the duties for the welfare of the people.

Bharata said with folded hands, "I have decided to go to the forest and bring Shri Rama back to Ayodhya. Only he has the right over the throne."

Hearing Bharata, all the people present praised him for his love, affection and sacrifice for his elder brother. A huge crowd of people accompanied Bharata in his mission to bring Lord Rama back to Ayodhya. It included all the queens, gurus and

ministers. For the protection from the wild animals a number of royal guards also accompanied them.

On the other side, when Lakshmana saw a huge crowd approaching them, he became worried. He climbed a tree and observed that an army was also there. He thought that Bharata had come to catch them.

So, Lakshmana started preparing himself for the big fight. Having seen Lakshmana in such an angry mood, Rama said, "Oh brother! Bharata is a person of very pious nature. He must have come here to meet me. So, do not suspect anything until his arrival."

Having heard Rama, Lakshmana became silent and started waiting for Bharata's arrival.

Soon Bharata reached Rama, Lakshmana and Sita. When he saw Rama in ordinary clothes, he fell on the feet of Rama and started weeping. He washed the feet of Rama with his tears.

Rama picked Bharata up and embraced him. Having seen Bharata after such a long time, Rama was also emotionally struck. Then, after gathering some courage Bharata said to Rama, "Our father could not tolerate the separation. He died with your name on his lips. Now, I came here to take you back to Ayodhya. Kindly come with us. Without you the people are orphaned. Please, sit on the throne which is your birthright."

After receiving the news of his father's death Lord Rama almost broke down. He also started weeping. Having seen Rama in such a bad condition, Bharata, Lakshmana and Sita consoled him. Actually they were all sad. Thereafter, Rama decided to offer libation to the soul of his father. Then, he went to the river Mandakini with Lakshmana and offered libation for his father's soul to rest in peace.

Kaikeyee was feeling sorry for her actions and was repentant.

When Rama returned from Mandakini, Kaikeyee fell on the feet of Rama and said, "I know that I have committed a sin and cannot be pardoned for that. Even then, I want you to forgive me and return home. The throne is rightfully yours and only you can sit on it."

Rama picked mother Kaikeyee up with great respect and said, "You are not at fault. It is all a game of fate. I cannot return to Ayodhya because I have to obey the order of my father. And this is the foremost duty of a person who belongs to Raghuvansha that they keep their promise by all means. Therefore, I cannot go back to Ayodhya. Rather, I will live in the forest for the whole period of my exile, that is fourteen years."

BHARATA RETURNS WITH RAMA'S SLIPPERS

After Kaikeyee, Bharata also began insisting on Lord Rama taking charge of Ayodhya. He said, "After the death of our father, Ayodhya became a city without a head or a guardian. Hence, we have come here to take you back to Ayodhya."

Having heard Bharata, Rama replied, "Bharata, you know that according to the convention of Raghukul we abide by our word at any cost. So I will keep the word of living in the forest for fourteen years. Don't be worried. I have Lakshmana and Sita to help me in my difficulties.

"As for you, you should go back to Ayodhya and fulfil your duties. Shatrughna will help you in your work and we all four brothers will continue to fulfill our respective duties. This is our religion, culture and convention."

Having heard Rama's advice, Bharata said, "Now, you are my father as well as my god. Your orders are a command for me. But I will not sit on the throne. Kindly, give me your wooden slippers I will keep them on the throne as a symbol of your presence. I will perform my duties taking inspiration from your slippers." Rama gave him his slippers. Thereafter, all the people returned to Ayodhya.

VIRADHA MEETS HIS END

After the return of Bharata to Ayodhya, Rama proceeded ahead from Chitrakoot. They reached the hut of a great sage Atri. On reaching there, they bowed to the sage and his wife Anusuya and got their blessings.

The sage and his wife showed great hospitality to Rama, Lakshmana and Sita. Sage Atri said to Rama as a request, "Kindly, stay with us tonight." Rama accepted the offer of the sage and stayed there that night.

In the morning, Rama took the permission of the sage and moved ahead. The forest was full of wild animals. The sounds of wild animals were echoing everywhere. Rama told Lakshmana to be alert for any danger.

All of a sudden, a giant demon Viradha attacked them and tried

to kill them. Rama and Lakshmana showered arrows at the demon but all the arrows fell on the ground after touching the body of the demon, Viradha.

Both Rama and Lakshmana were surprised to see this. They put their bows aside and caught hold of the demon. They pushed him on the ground and killed him by trampling him with their feet.

Then they went ahead in the forest.

After killing the demon Viradha, Rama went ahead into the forest. Walking for some time, they reached the hut of Agastya, a sage. Rama bowed to the sage. Seeing Rama, he became very happy. He extended a hearty welcome to him and said, "Rama, you have made my hut a sacred place to live. I am lucky to see you in my hut. This is the opportunity which I got by the blessings of the gods. Since you are omniscient you must have known that you are born with a great aim."

To stress his point, the sage further said, "The atrocities of the demons are increasing day by day. Because of the burden of sins committed by them, the earth is going down. Hence, you are requested to kill the demons to make this world a peaceful place where the sages and hermits can do religious work without fear. It is very difficult to perform yajna, recitation of verses and to do meditation in the present state. I cannot say anything else as you already know more than I do."

Hearing the sage, Rama said very politely, "O great sage! I will do what you expect from me. But right now I don't have a place to live. We are new in this forest, so we do not know much about it. Could you please tell us a proper and safe place where we can stay?" In reply to Rama's question, the sage said, "Panchvati is the best place for you. It is peaceful as well as safe. The greenery over there will make you happy."

Rama said, "The place suggested by you must be good. So, allow us to go." At the time of their departure, the sage gave Rama divine weapons and said, "Oh Raghunandan, take these weapons. These will help you in fighting with dangerous demons." Rama expressed his gratitude and took the weapons.

After taking the permission of the sage, they proceeded towards Panchvati. The route was long and they wanted to reach there before sunset. So, they kept on walking continuously without taking any rest.

The route to Panchvati passed through a dense forest. Rama faced many wild animals but continued the journey without any break. On their way, they met Jatayu who was the friend of their father. Jatayu assured them of his full help against the demons as well as wild animals.

Rama was very happy to meet Jatayu. His assurance further made him happy. Then they continued their journey to Panchvati and reached there before sunset.

Panchvati was a very beautiful place surrounded by natural beauty. Rama loved the place very much. He asked Lakshmana to build a hut at a proper place.

Lakshmana made the hut with the help of grass, mud and wood. Rama praised the intelligence and artistic view of Lakshmana. Having prepared beds of grass, they started living in Panchvati.

SHOORPANKHA PROPOSES TO RAMA

Rama was living in Panchvati along with Sita and Lakshmana. One morning, when they were sitting outside the hut, Shoorpankha, the sister of King Ravana was passing through that route. She saw Rama and fell in love with him.

Though Shoorpankha was an ugly looking demoness, she knew the art of changing her physical appearance. To attract Rama, she turned herself into a beautiful woman. Then she approached Rama and said, "How handsome you are! I want to marry you."

Having heard her, Rama smiled and said, "O beauty! I would be happy to marry you but I am already married. Go to my younger brother who is unmarried. You propose to him."

Shoorpankha turned her eyes to Lakshmana. When she looked at him, she found an attractive youth worth marrying. Hence, she ignored Rama and went to Lakshmana to propose to him.

Hearing her Lakshmana said, " You are very beautiful. But I am a servant of Rama. Will you like to marry a servant?"

Heaving heard Lakshmana's words, Shoorpankha became disappointed. Then she saw Sita with Rama. She then said to Rama, "So you have rejected me only because of this ugly woman. If it is so, I will kill her and then there would be no hinderance in our marriage. We both will live together happily."

Having said so, Shoorpankha turned to her real appearance of an ugly demoness. She rushed to kill Sita but before she could do that Lakshmana pounced on her and chopped off her nose and ears with his sword. She ran away crying with pain.

While crying, Shoorpankha threatened Rama and Lakshmana saying, "My brothers are the kings of this forest. They will make you suffer for what you have done to me. Nobody can save you now from your death."

Saying this, Shoorpankha rushed to her brothers Khara and Dushana who were kings and known for their bravery. She narrated the whole story to her brothers but skipped the part which could incriminate her. She shifted the whole blame on Rama and Lakshmana's shoulders for cutting her nose and ears.

To stir their anger, she further said, "If you are as brave as you claim to be, you will avenge my insult by killing both Rama and Lakshmana. But if you refuse to do so, I will tell the whole world that you are just cowards who pose to be brave."

Having heard the insulting comments of Shoorpankha, Khara and Dushana could not control their anger. They prepared a big army of demons and reached Panchvati. Rama was prepared for the attack. So, he sent Sita to a cave with Lakshmana. Rama came out of Panchvati to face the demons. As soon as they caught sight of Rama, the demons attacked him. Though Rama was alone, he faced the big army of demons very bravely. He showered arrows and killed all the demons of the army.

In the end, as soon as Khara and Dushana came forward to fight, Rama killed them both.

RAVANA GETS THE NEWS

After the big fight with Khara and Dushana, Lakshmana came out of the cave with Sita. They saw the piles of the dead bodies of the demons. Lakshmana hugged his brother.

One of the demons named Akampan managed to save himself and rushed to Ravana to inform him about the great disaster. As soon as he reached there, he informed Ravana about the killing of his brothers, Khara and Dushana along with the army. Ravana could not believe all this. He became angry.

He cried, "Who dared to kill my brothers and challenge me? Tell me, who killed them? I will go and kill them right now."

The demon Akampan said in a trembling voice, "O Lankesh! There are two young men from Ayodhya. They are the sons of Dasharatha, Rama and Lakshmana. Though they look like ordinary persons, they have killed the big army of fourteen thousand demons. They have also killed Khara and Dushana."

In a tremulous voice, Akampan further said, "Maharaj! Nobody can face Rama as he possesses some extraordinary powers. If anybody can face Rama, then it's you. But I advise you too that instead of facing Rama use some trick to kill him. I heard that Rama's wife, Sita is very beautiful and he loves Sita very much. If you kidnap Sita, Rama will die in the absence of Sita. This way you can take revenge of the death of your brothers."

Ravana liked the idea of Akampan. He thought deeply about the plan of kidnapping Sita. Then, he went to Mareech who was an expert in changing his form. Mareech welcomed Ravana and asked the reason for his visit.

Ravana told him, "Rama and Lakshmana have killed my brothers Khara and Dushana along with a great number of demons and I want to take revenge. So, I came here for your help. I want your help in kidnapping Sita. This is the easiest way to kill Rama as he will not be able to live long in the

absence of Sita. He will die lamenting for Sita. Having heard the plan of Ravana, Mareech became upset. He told Ravana in a censorious tone, "Oh mighty King Ravana! This is a very mean method of taking revenge. Whosoever gave you this advice can't be your friend. He must be your enemy. No wellwisher will give such an evil advice."

In the same stream he further said, "I am your wellwisher and that is why I am advising you not to kidnap Sita. If you kidnap Sita then the destruction of Lanka is for sure. Besides, all of your relatives and the people of Lanka will be killed."

Having heard Mareech's words, Ravana became silent. He gave his plan a second thought and decided not to execute it.

Thereafter, Ravana returned to Lanka dropping the idea of kidnapping Sita and started thinking of some other way of taking revenge for his brothers' killing.

Till now, he did not know the incident of Shoorpankha.

No sooner had Ravana sat on the throne after meeting Mareech that Shoorpankha appeared in his court. Her nose and ears were bleeding. Seeing her in such a pitiable condition, Ravana got furious and cried in anger, "Sister, who did this? Who is it that has lost his interest in his life?"

Having heard Ravana, Shoorpankha said, "Brother, while I was roaming in the forest I saw Sita, the beautiful wife of Rama. I thought that such a beautiful lady is perfect to become your wife. So, I tried to catch her, but Lakshmana cut my nose and ears. Now, you have to take revenge of my insult. The best way is to kidnap the wife of Rama. In this way you will get the beautiful woman and Rama will be punished."

Having heard the advice of Shoorpankha, Ravana again started thinking about kidnapping Sita. But, the words of Mareech were still echoing in his mind. Though Ravana himself was a learned person, his arrogance, anger, and ill fate destroyed his wisdom. So finally, he decided to kidnap Sita and proceeded to meet Mareech.

When Mareech asked him about the reason of his second visit Ravana said, "On your advice, I had dropped the idea of kidnapping Sita, but when I reached Lanka and saw the pitiable condition of my sister, Shoorpankha, I changed my mind. Now I have decided to take my revenge at any cost. I  know you are the most intelligent magician in the world. So, I need your help. I have devised a plan in which you will play an important part. Now listen, you will go in front of Rama's hut in the guise of a golden deer. Seeing a beautiful golden deer Sita would naturally get attracted towards it. She would ask her husband to bring it to her. When Rama and Lakshmana come after you, you will take them as far away from the hut as possible. Meanwhile, I will go to the hut and kidnap Sita."

Mareech replied politely, " I have tasted the power of arrow of Rama once. Hence, I cannot dare to taste it again."

Hearing the negative answer of Mareech, Ravana got angry. He said in a thunderous voice, "How dare you disobey me, I will kill you," saying so he drew his sword.

Mareech thought that it would be better to die with the arrow of Rama than of Ravana. So, he said, "If you are insisting so much, I will do what you have asked me to. However, I warn you that Rama is not an ordinary person and by causing trouble to them you are inviting your death." But Ravana stuck to his plan.

Mareech understood that Ravana has decided to follow the path of sin and he will not shift from his stand at any cost. So, he agreed.

Ravana was happy with Mareech. He said in an eager voice to Mareech, "Now we should go to Panchvati at once without any delay."

Ravana went to Panchvati with Mareech in his Pushpak Viman. On reaching there, Ravana said to Mareech, "Now you do your work as per our plan." He showed him the hut of Rama.

As per the desire of Ravana, Mareech started roaming in front of Rama's hut in the guise of a golden deer. When Sita saw it, she said to Rama, "See that golden deer. How beautiful it is! I want you to catch it for me." Seeing such a deer Rama and Lakshmana became very surprised. They had never seen a golden deer ever before anywhere in the forest.

Rama said, "This deer is different from others. So, I suspect that there may be a demon in the shape of that deer. Let that deer go. Here we are living in the middle of the forest. So, we must take precautions." But Sita insisted on Rama bringing the golden dear. She said to Rama, "I do not know anything. I want the golden deer at any cost."

Seeing the adamant attitude of Sita, Rama said to Lakshmana, "Since Sita is insisting on the deer, I am going to catch it. Take care of her as the forest is full of wild animals and demons.

"In my absence, do not leave her alone until I come back with the deer." After assigning Lakshmana the responsibility for the safety of Sita, Rama followed the deer into the forest.

As soon as Rama left the hut to chase the golden deer, Lakshmana took charge of the safety of Sita.

Rama followed the golden deer in an attempt to chase it. Seeing Rama coming behind him, Mareech, in the form of golden deer, ran away from the hut. Rama started chasing him. While running away from Rama, the deer entered the deep forest.

Rama also went deep into the forest behind the deer. After chasing him for a long time, Rama aimed an arrow at the deer and released it. After being hit by an arrow Mareech resumed his original shape. Whining with pain,

he imitated the voice of Rama and screamed, "Oh Sita! Oh Lakshmana! I am dying. Save me."

Hearing the voice of Rama, Sita got worried and said to Lakshmana, "Please, run and save your brother. He is in trouble."

Lakshmana knew that nobody has the power to kill Rama in the whole universe. So, he refused and said, "It is not the voice of Rama. It must be a demon who is imitating the voice of

Rama. So, do not worry. Nobody can do any harm to my brother Rama."

Hearing Lakshmana, Sita got furious and said, "You always obey your brother and treat him as a god. Now he is in trouble. Why don't you go and help him? Where is your love for him?" In reply to Sita's accusation, Lakshmana said, "Rama has given me the responsibility to safeguard you. So, I cannot leave you alone."

Sita again said, "I think your intention is wrong. You are making excuses." Hearing the false allegations, Lakshmana became very sad. He drew a line around the hut and said to Sita, "Do not come out of this line. It will protect you. If any one tries to cross the line he would be burnt alive."

Saying so, Lakshmana followed the cry of Rama with a heavy heart.

Lakshmana went away asking Sita not to cross the line.

After the departure of Lakshmana, Ravana who was hiding behind the bushes came out in the guise of a sage. He went to Sita and said, "Give me alms."

Hearing the sage, Sita came out of the hut with some fruits. She offered it to the sage but the sage refused. He said, "I don't take bound alms. If you want to give alms to me then cross the line." But Sita said, "I have not been permitted to cross the line. So, I cannot come out." When Sita refused to cross the line Ravana, in the guise of a sage, said, "This is against moral law. I will prefer to go empty handed instead of taking bound alms."

When Sita saw the sage going without alms, she thought she had committed a sin. So she asked Ravana to stop and crossed the line with alms for him. As soon as Sita crossed the line of protection, Ravana resumed his original form. He caught her by hair and took her to the Pushpak. Seeing Ravana, Sita got frightened and cried for help, "Oh Rama! Oh Lakshmana! Save me from the clutches of this demon."

JATAYU FIGHTS AGAINST RAVANA

Sita cried for help but no one was there to help her. While Ravana was taking her to Lanka, Jatayu, who was sitting on a high tree, saw a woman going by the route of the sky on a plane. He also heard her cries for help. Jatayu immediately followed the plane and found that Ravana was taking away Sita in his plane by force, so Sita was crying for help.

Jatayu flew in front of the plane and said to Ravana in an angry voice, "Leave Sita alone. Otherwise, I will kill you."

Ravana said, "Who are you to interfere? Get aside and let me go. Otherwise, I will kill you."

This argument caused a fight between Ravana and Jatayu. As Jatayu was old, he was unable to fight longer. Taking advantage of the situation, Ravana cut off his wings with his sword. Ravana again started his journey to Lanka on the plane.

When Rama saw the golden deer in its original form of a demon, Mareech, he immediately guessed the trick. He was very worried about the safety of Sita. He thought, 'What would happen if on hearing the call of Mareech, Lakshmana had followed me leaving Sita alone.' So, he quickly rushed to the hut.

While Rama was on his way to the hut, he saw Lakshmana coming towards him. He got angry with Lakshmana and said, "Why did you come here leaving Sita alone. I had directed you not to leave Sita alone under any circumstances. My instincts are telling me that something bad has happened to Sita. I cannot live without Sita. You should not have left her alone." Rama continued to speak in a fit of nervousness and kept on moving fast to the hut.

Hearing about Rama's doubts, Lakshmana's eyes filled with tears. He said to Rama with folded hands, "I told mother Sita so many times that the cry was not yours, but she insisted that I should follow you. Believe me. I did not disobey you."

After some time, when both the brothers reached the hut and found Sita missing, they became very sad. They saw some fruits and pots scattered at the gate of the hut.

Rama called Sita several times but there was no response. Both were very worried and started searching for Sita everywhere.

Rama asked each and every tree, bird, river and drain about Sita but the brothers found her nowhere. While roaming in the forest they reached the place where Jatayu was breathing his last.

When Rama and Lakshmana saw Jatayu wounded, they picked him up and asked, "Tell us, who wounded you?" With these words, Rama picked him up in his lap.

Jatayu replied with great difficulty, "I am alive only to tell you that Ravana has kidnapped your wife Sita. I tried my best to stop him but he cut my wings. I am sorry that I could not save Sita," saying so Jatayu died.

Hearing this, Rama became very sad. On the one hand, he was worried about Sita while on the other hand, he had lost his devotee and protector in the forest. He decided to perform the last rites of Jatayu who lost his life while protecting Sita.

THE ONE-EYED DEMON

After the death of Jatayu, Rama was very upset. He performed the last rites of Jatayu and then went ahead in search of Sita. Now he was sure that Sita was kidnapped by Ravana, the king of Lanka. So, he was very sad.

While searching for Sita, Rama reached a forest known as Kroanch. There he saw a dreaded demon who had only one eye and two long teeth appearing outside his each jaw. As soon as he saw Rama and Lakshmana he caught them with his huge hands. Both the brothers looked like toys in his hands.

Both tried their best to release themselves from the clutches of the demon but they failed.

The demon lifted them up and was about to swallow them. All of a sudden, Rama managed to take out his sword and

cut his arms off. The wound inflicted by Rama killed the demon.

Thereafter, Rama threw his body in the fire. As soon as the dead body got burnt, a handsome youth appeared. He came to Rama with folded hands and said, "I am a Gandharva. My name is Kabandha. A curse had made me a demon. You have freed me from the curse."

He further said, "I am thankful to you for making me free of the curse. I advise you to go to Sugreeva. He will help you in your search for mother Sita." Rama asked him the address of Sugreeva. Kabandha told him, "Go straight to Pampa. There you would see mother Shabri. She will tell you everything about Sugreeva." Saying this, Kabandha disappeared.

MEETING WITH SHABRI

Shabri was a deciple of the sage Matanga and a devotee of Rama. Long ago the sage had said to Shabri, "One day, Lord Vishnu himself would appear before you." Since then Shabri was waiting for Rama to come to her hut.

According to the advice of Kabandha, Rama went to Pampa. There he saw an ordinary hut. It was the hut of Shabri. Seeing Rama, Shabri fell at his feet and said, "Oh Lord! I have been waiting for you for such a long time. I am so happy that you have finally come." Saying this, tears rolled out from her eyes. Then, she spread a cloth for both the brothers to sit on.

Shabri had already collected berries from the forest for Rama. She did not want to give them sour berries. So, before serving them, she herself tasted them and gave them only the sweet ones. Rama ate the berries but Lakshmana did not like the idea of eating the half-eaten fruit. So, he threw them secretly aside.

Thereafter, Rama asked her about Sugreeva. Shabri said, "Sugreeva is living on the mountain Rishyamooka with his friends. The place is not very far from here." Rama proceeded to Rishyamooka mountain as directed by Shabri.

RAMA AND LAKSHMANA ON RISHYAMOOKA

Rama was very worried about Sita. He kept on searching for her on the way to the mountain range of Rishyamooka. At times, he lamented for her and Lakshmana had to console him. Lakshmana was very sad on seeing Rama in such a pitiable condition. They reached the residence of Sugreeva.

When Sugreeva's spy informed him that Rama and Lakshmana were approaching him, he thought that his brother must have sent someone to kill him. So, he asked Hanumana to meet the visitors and find out the reason for their visit. He said, "Go in disguise as a priest and ask them who they are, where they have come from why they have come here."

Hanumana went to Rama and Lakshmana in disguise of a priest. He said to them, "Would you like to introduce yourself? Though you are dressed like the people who live in the forest, you look like princes. Your feet do not look accustomed to walking on a rough ground."

Seeing Hanumana's curiosity Lakshmana said, "This is my elder brother Rama and I am Lakshmana. You have guessed correctly. We are the princes of Ayodhya. We were living in exile for some time but the activities of the demon Ravana have perturbed us. He has kidnapped Mata Sita. We are going here and there in search of her. The Gandharva named Kabandha told us that Sugreeva will help us. So, we came here to meet Sugreeva. Do you know anything about him?"

Hanumana knew that Lord Vishnu has incarnated himself as Rama. So, he changed his form and appeared as Hanumana. Then, he fell at Rama's feet and said, "Oh Lord! I am the prime minister of Sugreeva. I have been worshipping you since my childhood. I think myself lucky because I have got an opportunity to serve my lord today."

After a pause, Hanumana again said, "I will take you to our king Sugreeva. He is living near the mountain. He would surely be happy to meet you. I believe that you will become good friends," saying this, Hanumana made them sit on his shoulders and flew away to Sugreeva. He landed them on the mountain and went to inform Sugreeva. While meeting Sugreeva, Hanumana told him in a very excited voice, "O Monkey King! They are the princes of Ayodhya—Rama and Lakshmana. They are spending the days of exile of fourteen years as per the desire of their step mother."

Hanumana further said, "Mata Sita also accompanied them but the king of Lanka, Ravana has kidnapped her. They have come here while searching for her. They want your help in this search. They both are brave and patient. I believe that they can be helpful to you in recovering your kingdom and wife from Bali. So, we should befriend them."

Having heard this, Sugreeva immediately went to Rama with Hanumana. The latter introduced Sugreeva to Rama and Lakshmana. Sugreeva also disclosed his problem to Rama, "My Lord! I was faithful to my elder brother, Bali. Unfortunately, one day a demon named Mayavi came to the city and a fierce fight took place between my brother and the demon. During the fight, the demon entered a cave. Bali asked me to wait at the gate of the cave and entered the cave to follow the demon. After some time I heard the cry of Bali and also saw blood coming out of the cave. I thought that the demon had killed my brother. I was afraid of the demon and thought that he would kill others too. So, I put a heavy stone at the gate of the cave for our safety.

"Thereafter, I returned to the city. Then, with the consent of all others, I occupied the throne and was declared the king of Kishkindha state."

In the same stream, Sugreeva further said, "Actually, Bali was not killed by the demon. Anyhow, he came out of the cave and presented himself in the royal court before all courtiers. He scolded and thrashed me. He also took away my wife forcibly. I was unable to face him as he was gifted with a boon that the opponent's half power would be merged with him. He wanted to kill me. That is why I am living on this mountain to save my life. He cannot come here due to the curse of a sage Matanga." Rama said, " Since you are my friend, I will help you as much as I can."

Sugreeva said, "I will also try my best to locate Mata Sita. I have a big army of monkeys and bears. They will go all around in all the directions." Then, Sugreeva showed some ornaments which were thrown by Sita. There were a necklace, earrings and many other things. Lakshmana could not recognise them because he

had never even seen her face. But if any of the ornaments of her feet were there, he would certainly recognize them as he used to touch her feet to take blessings daily.

Rama could not control himself on seeing the ornaments of Sita. He lamented loudly. Lakshmana and Sugreeva consoled Rama.

Thereafter, Rama and Sugreeva took pledge of friendship in the presence of all with fire as witness. They promised to remain friends throughout their lives. They also promised to share all their sorrows and happiness together. Rama said to Sugreeva, "Go and challenge Bali to fight. I will shoot an arrow to kill him hiding myself behind the trees."

Then Rama, Lakshmana and Sugreeva reached Kishkindha.

Sugreeva challenged Bali and the fight started. Rama hid himself behind the trees and poised an arrow on the bow. But he was surprised to see the similarities between the two brothers. Even the way of fighting was the same. So, he was unable to identify Bali. The fight continued for a long time. Sugreeva was surprised to see that Rama was not hitting Bali as was planned. Then, the fight ended on sunset.

After the end of the bout when Sugreeva asked Rama why he did not hit Bali during the fight, Rama said, "There are so many similarities between you and Bali that I became confused. So, I was hesitating in shooting the arrow."

Thereafter, Rama said Sugreeva, "Now I suggest you fight again but wear a garland. So that I can identify Bali."

Next day, Sugreeva again challenged Bali for a bout. Bali was proud of his power and strength so he readily agreed to fight again. At this moment his wife Tara said, "Lord, this time you should not fight with Sugreeva. I had a bad dream yesterday. I advise you to reconcile and compromise with your younger brother so that both of you live in peace."

But Bali ignored her advice and went out in a great anger. Then, he reached Sugreeva and said, "Yesterday, I did not kill you but today nobody can save you. Your death has brought you here." Sugreeva said, "Time will tell who is going to die to day."

Again, a fight started between Bali and Sugreeva. Bali threw Sugreeva down twice and appeared to be stronger than him. At this moment, Rama shot an arrow at Bali. It pierced Bali's chest. As soon as the arrow hit Bali, he fell to the ground and started crying in pain.

The sad news reached the palace. His wife Tara who was already worried about him, came running to him.

She started lamenting, "Lord! Had you followed my advice, this day of sorrow would not have come into our lives and your son Angada would not have become an orphan."

Bali was breathing his last. He said to Sugreeva, "My end is very near. Take care of Tara and Angada." Having said this, Bali died. After the death of Bali, all of them started for the city of Kishkindha.

Now, it was certain that Sugreeva would become the king of Kishkindha. Also, he was supposed now to take charge of his brother's wife Tara and their son Angada.

THE SEARCH FOR SITA

After the death of Bali, Sugreeva was placed on the throne of Kishkindha by Rama. Sugreeva ruled the city and kept himself busy with the state affairs. On the other hand, Rama was waiting anxiously for Sugreeva to come to help him in his search of Sita but Sugreeva did not turn up. Hanumana was feeling bad so he went to Sugreeva and said, "My Lord! You have forgotten the promise made to Rama who has made you the king and lost yourself in the luxuries of royal life."

Hearing Hanumana, Sugreeva came to his senses. He said, "I am really sorry and now I will do everything in my power to help you in the search for Sita." Thereafter, he organised a big army of monkeys and bears and went to Rama. He bowed to Rama and said, "I am sorry that I was delayed in coming to help you. Now I am sending my soldiers in different directions to search for Sita. They will definitely find her."

The soldiers of Sugreeva searched everywhere for Sita but in vain. Seeing this, Rama became worried. His anxiety was increasing day by day.

One day, he said to the Hanumana, "I believe that only you are able to reach Sita. So, keep this ring with you and go to the south. When you find Sita, give this ring to her and she will come to know that you are my messenger."

Taking the signet ring of Rama, Hanumana proceeded to the south. Several months passed. Almost all the soldiers of Sugreeva came back without any success but Rama never lost hope. He had a firm belief that Hanumana would definitely find Sita. While, on the other hand, having passed several weeks in searching for Sita. Hanumana and his companions saw a cave. Having entered the cave, they saw a garden full of fruits, flowers and other trees. There was a golden palace as well. They had never seen such a palace before. They were tired of roaming in search of Sita. So, they were hungry and thirsty. The juicy fruits of the garden attracted them so much that they entered it. The beauty of the garden filled their hearts with happiness.

Having entered the garden, Hanumana and Angada saw a virtuous woman sitting on a beautiful throne. Her face was shining with a divine glow. When Hanumana asked her who she was, she answered, "I am Swayamprabha. This city is constructed by the architect of demons, Maya. Nobody can enter the city without my consent. I also know that you are searching for Mata Sita. So, I have pardoned you for your mischievous behaviour and am sending you out of this cave by using my supernatural powers. You have to do a lot of work."

Swayamprabha sent them out of the cave by using her divine power. They found themselves lying on the seashore. Sitting there, Hanumana and Jambavan started discussing what to do next. Since the rainy season was approaching fast, their difficulties were also increasing. They were very worried because the given period to search Sita was about to be over. How would they show their faces to Rama and Sugreeva? Angada pledged not to take food till Sita was found.

COOPERATION OF A GREAT VULTURE

The great vulture Sampati was listening to the conversation of Hanumana and Jambavan. When he heard the pledge undertaken by Angada he became happy. He thought, 'Now, I would be able to eat human flesh.' But next moment his happiness vanished when he heard a monkey saying, "Jatayu was far better than us who sacrificed his life while protecting Sita from the demon. We are not even able to trace Sita by now."

When Sampati heard about the death of Jatayu, tears started rolling out of his eyes. Jatayu was his brother. He consoled himself by thinking that Jatayu sacrificed his life for a good cause. He also flew high to trace Sita and succeeded in finding her. So, he went to Hanumana and Jambavan. He introduced himself to them and then said, "The king of Lanka has hidden

Sita in the garden of Ashoka trees which is one hundred miles away across the sea." They all were happy to know about Sita. But now, they had another problem to face. Who would go across the sea to reach Sita?

All of them started thinking deeply to find the solution of this problem. The capacity of each one was considered individually turn by turn. Gaja was capable of crossing the sea measuring ten yojans, Gavaksha could cross twenty yojans and Jambavan could cross ninety yojans, but Lanka was hundred yojans away from the seashore. Though Angada was capable of crossing hundred yojans, the problem was that after crossing hundred yojans, he would become so tired that he wouldn't be able to complete the return journey.

THE PRAISE OF HANUMANA

Jambavan observed that Hanumana was silent. He went to him and said, "Oh Son of Air! You are not taking part in the discussion. Why are you sitting here silently?"

Hanumana said, "I am also thinking about crossing the sea. But just like all others, I also don't know whether I would be able to cross the sea or not." Jambavan said to Hanumana in an encouraging tone, "You are the son of air so you can go faster than anyone else. You have the capacity to cross the sea in one step. Now, you have got an opportunity to show your might. You must take advantage of this opportunity." But Hanumana said nothing. He was not influenced by the praise of Jambavan.

Seeing that Hanumana was not responding to his earnest urgings, Jambavan further said, "Your mother was the goddess Anjani. She took birth in the monkey clan due to a curse. It was by chance that Vayudev fell in love with her. So, being the son

of Vayudev, you are equally powerful and capable. Don't you remember that once during your childhood days, you swallowed the sun thinking it to be a fruit. To protect the sun, Lord Indra attacked you with his Vajra because of which you got wounded and fell to the ground. Seeing this, Vayudev stopped blowing. It created a wave of terror. The people were not able to breathe in the absence of air. Then, all the gods went to Vayudev and begged his pardon. Since then, you are known as 'Ajatshatru' that means without any enemy.

Even after hearing stories of his might from Sampati, Hanumana kept mum. Then Jambavan said, "Recognise your power and strength. You have unlimited power and strength. Your ideals, decency and dignity have made you great. I have gone around the world for twenty one times. But even then, I think of you to be greater than myself. You are the only hope for us. Only you can cross the sea."

Hearing Jambavan, Hanumana became excited. He regained the power and strength which was lost by the curse of a sage. He realised the seriousness of the situation. He got up and let the size of his body increase. Seeing his wide and broad body all of them were very surprised. They prayed to Hanumana to cross the sea and go to Lanka. So, he finally decided to go to Lanka.

HANUMANA LEAVES FOR LANKA

Hanumana said, "Jambavan, I will fly to Lanka right now. I am ready to do anything for Shri Rama. Now nobody can stop me from going there. Kindly wait for my return from Lanka." saying this, Hanumana flew away to Lanka.

On his way to Lanka, a mountain named Mayank came up from the sea and said , "My son, your route is long. So, take rest here for some time. You will become fresh again and your journey would be easier."

Hanumana replied, "O King of the Mountains, I am grateful to you for your kindness, but I am in a hurry. I have to perform a very important task. When I return, I will sit with you. Now bless me so that I can perform my duty well," saying this, Hanumana again resumed his journey to Lanka.

As soon as Hanumana bid goodbye to Mayank and flew ahead, a big demoness named Sursa appeared from the sea. She was purposely sent by the gods to test the capability of Hanumana.

Sursa came before Hanumana and stopped his way. She opened her mouth to one yojan and tried to swallow Hanumana. But he also increased his size. Seeing this, Sursa started increasing the size of her mouth. When Hanumana realized that Sursa can broaden her mouth to hundred yojans he reduced himself to the size of a thumb. Then, he quickly entered her mouth and came out of it immediately.

Sursa was pleased with Hanumana's cleverness. She blessed Hanumana for the success of his mission.

Having met with Sursa, Hanumana resumed his journey to Lanka. While he was flying over the sea, another demoness saw his reflection in the water and caught him. Hanumana quickly entered her mouth and tore away her belly. She died instantly. This way the sea got relief from another wicked being.

After facing many obstacles and hindrances, Hanumana finally

entered Lanka. The high trees of
coconut looked like guards. Cool and
fragrant air was blowing slowly. Hanumana landed
on the high Trikoot mountain and observed the prosperity of
Lanka. It was situated on a seashore. The whole of Lanka was
surrounded by high walls. The buildings were high and had
golden polish. Hanumana had never seen such a beautiful city
before. It was protected by soldiers.

So, Hanumana decided to enter the city at night. At the gate of
Lanka, he took the blessings of the goddess of the garden,
Lankini and entered the city in the form of an ordinary monkey.
He started jumping from one parapet to another. He peeped into
all the houses but could not find Sita. Then, he climbed to the
palace of Ravana and reached his private room. There, he saw
several women, Gandharava girls and demonesses, but Sita was
not there. He went to the queens' residence and searched for
Sita all over the palace but found her nowhere.

Hanumana went to other houses after visiting the palace. While he was passing through the houses he heard *Rama-Rama* coming from a house. He was surprised to see the flag on the house with inscription of Rama written on it. When he peeped into the house out of curiosity, he saw there an ordinary person worshipping Lord Rama.

Hanumana appeared before him in his original form. Having seen Hanumana, the man became nervous. To assuage his fear, Hanumana said, "Don't be afraid of me. I just want to know who is worshipping Rama in this city?"

He said, "I am the brother of Ravana. My name is Vibhishana and I am a devotee of Rama. Ravana does not like it. So, I live away from his palace in this ordinary house. Now, I am spending my days by worshipping Lord Rama."

After finding out that Vibhishana was a devotee of Rama, Hanumana said, "Kindly accept my greetings." After saying this, Hanumana folded his hands and started explaining the

reason of his visit to him, "I have come here in search of Sita, but could not find her. Could you, please tell me where Ravana has kept her? She is not in the palace of Ravana."

Hearing Hanumana, Vibhishana said, "Ravana has imprisoned Sita in Ashok Vatika. It is adjacent to his palace."

Hanumana said goodbye to Vibhishana and proceeded to Ashok Vatika. The garden was surrounded by high walls. There was no entry gate. Hence, Hanumana sat on the top of a tree.

He was very happy to see the tree bearing fruits and flowers. There were beautiful fountains and springs as well.

Thereafter, Hanumana climbed up to the highest tree in the garden and started observing the garden.

While inspecting Ashok Vatika, Hanumana saw a lean and thin woman sitting under a tree. A pain of separation was quite visible on her face. Seeing her Hanumana concluded that she must

be the Sita. She was being guarded by several black and ugly demonesses. They all had weapons with them. In between those demonesses, Sita looked like a diamond among coals. She was sitting silently in a corner of the garden. Hanumana was very much eager to meet Sita but it was not possible in the presence of the demonesses.

Hanumana thought, 'I have to take each and every step with great precaution. I will wait for the proper time.' Thinking so, he sat behind the leaves of a tree and waited for the evening.

Hanumana was observing the scene of the Vatika sitting on the branch of a tree. Suddenly, he saw Ravana coming towards Sita. He was dressed in royal silk clothes and his face was shining with his deep knowledge and wisdom. He went to Sita and said, "Oh beauty! I once again offer myself to you and propose to marry you. You will be the head queen and have all comforts and luxuries. I will fulfill each and every desire of yours."

Hearing Ravana, Sita turned her face away and said, "Oh sinner, tyrant and cheater! Keep your hands away from me, you coward! You kidnapped me, in the absence of my husband. This

is very bad and you would be burnt in the fire of my husband's anger. If you want to live, go to my husband and ask for his forgiveness."

Having heard these words, Ravana became furious and ordered the demonesses saying, "Terrify this stubborn woman and make her marry me."

Hanumana was very angry to see the behaviour of Ravana but after seeing the seriousness of the situation he kept mum. The demonesses forced Sita to accept the proposal of Ravana but Trijata stopped them. She was a kind-hearted demoness. She used to treat Sita like her daughter.

She went to Sita and said, "Do not afraid! I saw in my dream that Shri Rama has come to take you and Lanka was burning. Ravana was killed.".

Having heard these words, Sita said, "I can only hope that your dream would soon come true."

After saying so, Sita became very sad and tears started rolling down from her eyes.

HANUMANA MEETS SITA

After some time, the demonesses guarding Sita went away leaving Sita alone. On seeing Sita alone, Hanumana started singing the song of greatness of Lord Rama. On hearing the praises of Rama, Sita became emotional and tears rolled down from her eyes. She was also surprised to hear Rama's praise in Lanka. So, she said, "Who are you? Who is singing Rama's songs. Please, show me your face."

Hearing this, Hanumana jumped from the tree and presented himself before Sita. He was in his original form. He bowed to Sita with folded hands and said to her. "I am Hanumana, a servant of Rama, I have been sent by him to make sure that you

are okay. Do not worry. Soon, Lord Rama along with Lakshmana will come and free you of this prison of Ravana. I have come here to give you this information."

But Sita who was living among the demons of magical powers refused to believe him. She said, "The demons' magical powers rule here. You must be a demon who is misusing the name of Rama to confuse me. It may be a new trick of Ravana."

When Sita expressed her doubts, Hanumana showed the signet ring given to him by Rama and said, "Lord Rama gave it to me to show you." Sita recognised the ring and touched it to her forehead. Then, she said to Hanumana, "I am sorry that I doubted you. You are really a devotee of Rama. Give my message to him to take me from here at once."

"As you wish," saying so, Hanumana bowed to Sita and took her blessings. As soon as he was about to go back to Rama, an idea struck his mind, 'Let me judge the capacity of the enemy before leaving Lanka.' So Hanumana started jumping from one tree to another and picking up the fruits. He also uprooted many trees. In this way he ruined the Ashok Vatika totally. Seeing the destruction of the garden, the guards tried to stop Hanumana but failed. Hanumana attacked also the guards and made them run for their lives. They asked the soldiers to stop Hanumana but Hanumana attacked them too with his club and knocked them down.

Hanumana changed the form and shape of the garden very quickly. He was not eating the fruits but throwing them on the ground along with their branches.

Most of the trees were uprooted. It appeared as if a storm broke there.

When Ravana received the news that a big monkey has ruined Ashok Vatika, he asked his son Akshay Kumar to arrest the monkey and bring him to the court. Akshay Kumar went to Ashok Vatika along with a big army of demons. He spread the soldiers all over the garden to catch Hanumana but none was able to catch him. He was alone fighting with the demons.

At last, Hanumana uprooted a big tree and threw it on the demons army. It fell on Akshay Kumar and his army. Most of the army got crushed to death under it. On seeing this, the rest of the soldiers became terrified and fled to save their lives.

Having received the news of his son's death Ravana become furious and called his elder son, Meghnada. He ordered him to arrest Hanumana and present him before the court. Meghnada was very brave warrior. He possessed many divine powers and heavenly weapons. Once he had defeated the god Indra and acquired the title of Inderjeet.

Meghnada went to Ashok Vatika and challenged Hanumana, "You have killed the children and the weak. If you think of yourself to be a hero, come and fight with me."

Then a fierce fight started between them. Meghnada used all the weapons against Hanumana but they all proved futile. At last he applied Brahamastra on him. Seeing this, Hanumana thought, 'If it proves it to be ineffective, it would be the insult to this heavenly weapon.' So he pretended to be struck by the weapon and fell to the ground. Meghnada tied him up and took him to the palace. On the way to the palace women and children saw Hanumana with great surprise. They had never seen such a big monkey before in their lives.

Meghnada presented Hanumana before Ravana in the court. Hanumana was very impressed by the pomp and grandeur of the Ravana's court. Ravana was sitting on the golden throne. The walls of the palace were decorated with the diamonds and precious stones.

Ravana asked Hanumana in an inquiring tone, "Oh Monkey! You are a very strange creature. Who sent you here? Indra or Kuber or someone else? Who are you and why have you uprooted the garden?"

Hanumana replied, "I am a messenger of Shri Rama and the prime minister of Sugreeva, the king of Kishkindha. My name is Hanumana and I am son of the god of air, Vayudev and Anjani. You have brought Mata Sita here against her will. Send her back immediately. There is still time for you to correct your mistake. Otherwise the whole of the demon clan will perish."

Hearing this, Ravana became furious and cried, "Kill this mischievous monkey." As the guards rushed to kill Hanumana, Vibhishana stopped them and said, "Hanumana is a messenger

and a messenger cannot be killed." Ravana accepted this but he wanted to teach Hanumana a lesson. So, Ravana decided to burn his tail as a punishment. Having received the orders of Ravana, his soldiers set Hanumana's tail on fire.

Hanumana jumped over the houses and palaces with his burning tail. The burning tail further burnt the houses of Lanka. Soon, the whole of the Lanka started burning. The golden Lanka was reduced to ashes. It was unexpected and the people rushed out of their burning houses to save themselves.

After burning Lanka, Hanumana dipped his tail in the sea to put out the fire. Then, he went to Mata Sita to take her permission to go back to Rama. Sita already knew about the orders of Ravana. So, she was praying for the safety of Hanumana.

When Hanumana reached her, she became very happy to see him safe and sound. She said, "I was very worried about your safety. Are you alright?"

Hanumana replied, "I am alright. Who can harm me when I have been under your blessings? I burnt the whole Lanka with the help of my tail. This will serve as a lesson to Ravana."

In the same stream, he further said, "Now, I want to go back to Rama to tell him about you. I will ask him to come here sooner to get you released from this prison of the demon, Ravana. I request you not to worry much and have patience as Shri Rama would be here at any time. I also request you to please give me

something as a memento by showing which I can prove that I have really met you."

Hearing Hanumana, Sita smiled slowly and gave her bangle to him. Hanumana, took the bangle and bowed to her. Thereafter, he returned to Rama.

Hanumana crossed the sea and reached the spot where Jambavan, Angada and others were waiting for him. Seeing Hanumana, all the monkeys became happy and started dancing with joy. They cried with happiness, "See! Hanumana has come back. Our protector has come back. He must have brought some good news for us."

Hanumana met all of them and narrated everything from the beginning to the end. They all surrounded Hanumana to hear him. Everybody was eager to know about the obstacles he faced during his journey to Lanka.

When Hanumana narrated his meeting with Mata Sita, they all became very happy to know that Mata Sita is alright. He said, "Now, we should go to Rama and tell him about the well being and whereabouts of Mata Sita. This will relieve him from some of his fears." All of them agreed.

Soon, they reached the royal garden of Sugreeva. They all were hungry and ate fruits on the trees to satisfy their hunger. Thereafter, they went to Rama, Lakshmana and Sugreeva.

Hanumana bowed to all and said, "I have got the address of Sita. The king of Lanka has imprisoned her in Ashok Vatika. When I met her she was sitting under a tree and remembering you. She is a faithful and simple woman. Hence, even if Ravana touches her he will get burnt alive."

He further said, "When I met her she asked me to give her a proof first. She thought that I am a demon who is playing a trick by using my magical power. But when I showed her your ring she recognised it immediately. Then, Mata Sita touched it to her forehead with great devotion. She gave me her bangle for you," After saying so, Hanumana took the bangle out and gave it to Rama. Seeing the bangle, Rama became emotional and started weeping profusely. Then, he thanked Hanumana by saying, "You have given me a new life by telling me that Sita is safe. How can I repay you for what you did for me?"

Hanumana said, "Do not say such words. I just did my duty. Now we should attack Lanka immediately to set Mata Sita free."

Thereafter, they started making plans of attacking Lanka but there was a big problem, that is, to cross the sea. Lord Rama invited everyone's suggestion to solve this problem. So, all of them started thinking of the methods by which they could cross the sea. First they decided to go to the seashore.

MARCH TO THE SEASHORE

Sugreeva said, "I think that Hanumana should carry Rama and Lakshmana on his shoulders and take them to the seashore. I and my army will follow him. Let us march to the seashore."

Hanumana took Rama and Lakshmana to the seashore on his shoulders. The army also reached there. Then, all of them camped in the forest near the seashore.

Rama said to Sugreeva, "Friend! We have come to the seashore with our big army but the problem of crossing the sea is still there. The sea is so deep that it cannot be swum across. Nor can it be jumped across. Then, how would we cross the sea?"

Having heard Rama, Sugreeva said, "Please, do not worry about it. We are thinking and soon the problem will be solved. We will do something to cross the sea."

On the other side, Ravana was feeling very angry as well as ashamed of how a monkey killed his son and uprooted Ashok Vatika. Not only this, he also burnt the city. He must be a monkey having supernatural powers.

Ravana guessed at some trouble and called a meeting of all the courtiers including chiefs of army. Almost all the courtiers of Ravana were flatterers. So, they said, "Oh king of Lanka! There is none equivalent to you in any respect. So, do not worry about the monkey. He must be a mischievous creature who has come here to create a disturbance. The security system of Lanka is unique. No one can break it."

The brother of Ravana named Vibhishana was also present there. He said, "Brother, these courtiers are just a bunch of flatterers. Don't believe them. They are talking just to please you. Otherwise, their talks are baseless. So, beware of these flattering people and take your own decision. It is a blunder to bring Sita here. I advise you to return Sita to Rama and save yourself from sin. There is still time to repent. Rama is very

kind and he will pardon you."

Hearing Vibhishana talking in favour of Rama, Ravana became furious. He said to him, "How dare you oppose me and praise Rama in my kingdom. You are my brother, but instead of helping me you are taking the side of my enemy. There is no place for you in Lanka. Get out from here immediately." Vibhishana tried to convince Ravana that he was in his favour but failed. Then he said, "It appears that your end is very near. Otherwise, you wouldn't have ignored my good advice. Take care of yourself, my brother, there is still time to correct your mistake," saying this, Vibhishana went away.

After Ravana exiled his brother Vibhishana, the latter decided to go to Rama and seek shelter there. He crossed the sea in his plane and reached the other side. He went straight to Rama and bowed to him. "My Lord! I am the brother of Ravana. My name is Vibhishana. My brother has exiled me. Now, I request you to take me in your shelter."

Rama said, "Vibhishana, do not worry. You can stay here as long as you wish."

But Sugreeva opposed it, he said, "My Lord! Think again. How can the brother of Ravana be our friend? Ravana is our enemy and his brother could be a spy."

Rama said, "Sugreeva, remember that at present Vibhishana is in our shelter. We must protect the person who comes to us for shelter." Having heard Rama's words, Sugreeva became silent.

RAMA PRAYS TO SEA

Rama consulted Sugreeva, Hanumana and Vibhishana on the problem of crossing the sea. It was decided that Rama would undertake a fast to please the god of the sea. They thought, 'If the god of the sea becomes pleased with Rama, he would give the way himself, and the army of Rama would be able to cross the sea to reach Lanka. Accordingly, Rama went on a fast and worshipped the sea. He prayed for three days and nights continuously to please the sea but the sea god did not appear.

Seeing this, Rama lost his patience and became furious. He threw a fire arrow into the heart of the sea. The fire arrow produced so much heat that the creatures of the sea started burning alive. Even the sea was not able to tolerate the heat of the fire for a long a time.

Ultimately, the god of the sea appeared before Rama with folded hands. He bowed to Rama and said, "Please, be patient and try to understand my situation. I cannot go beyond the laws of nature. But I can suggest to you a method by which you can cross the sea. There are two monkeys named Nala and Neela in your army. Being the sons of Vishwakarma, they are great architects. They can make a bridge with the help of big stones and branches of the trees. With the help of this bridge, your army can reach Lanka easily."

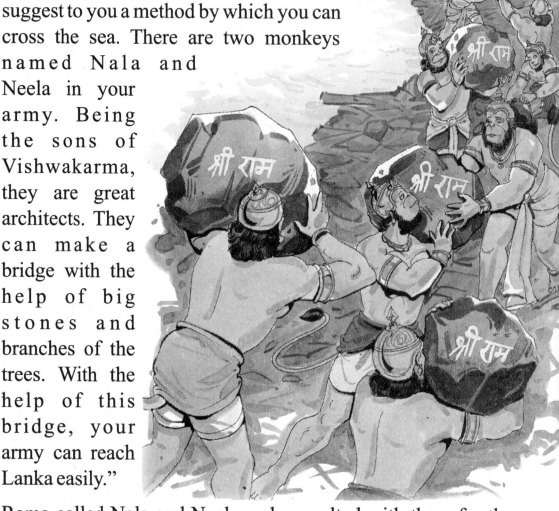

Rama called Nala and Neela and consulted with them for the construction of the bridge. Thereafter, Rama asked the monkeys to go to the nearby forest to bring stones and trees. Soon, the stones and trees were piled up near the sea.

Nala and Neela used their skill to construct the bridge on the sea. Under their direction monkeys and bears constructed a bridge over the sea. It covered the distance of one hundred yojans and stretched up to the land of Lanka. It was a work worth praising and gods showered flowers over it.

Ravana made several efforts to woo Sita but did not succeed. In the meanwhile, he came to know that the army of Rama had reached the seashore and it may enter Lanka at any time.

Under the circumstances, he decided to make a fresh effort to coax Sita. This time he used demons' magical power. He asked a magician named Vidutjiva to prepare a dummy of Rama. Then, he took the head of that dummy and showed it to Sita and said, "See your husband is killed and now you are mine for ever." Seeing this, Sita started weeping and said, "It is not possible. I would prefer to die rather than marrying you." Ravana returned to his palace with anger and disappointment.

At this moment, Trijata appeared there. She told Sita , "That was not the head of Rama. It was all demons' magical power. The fact is that Rama and Lakshmana have reached the border of Lanka and soon they will enter the city of Lanka. Now, you will meet your husband very soon and you will be out of this prison also." After hearing it, Sita became relieved.

SUGREEVA ATTACKS RAVANA

Ravana returned to his palace from Ashok Vatika after making a fruitless effort to woo Sita. He went up to the roof of the palace to watch the army of Rama. He saw that monkeys and bears were climbing on the houses, trees and streets of the city. Seeing them, he became worried and started thinking of ways to stop them. Actually, he wanted to kill all of them at once.

Sugreeva was marching ahead with his army towards Lanka. When he saw Ravana standing on the roof of the palace he became furious. He said, "Oh! This is Ravana who kidnapped Mata Sita. I must teach him a lesson." Saying this he jumped to the palace roof and started beating him. Ravana retaliated by hitting him back.

Since Ravana

was more powerful than Sugreeva, the latter soon realized that he would not be able to kill Ravana alone. So, he returned to Rama. Rama was observing the fight. Seeing Sugreeva coming back he became happy and said, "You made a mistake by challenging Ravana alone. Since you are a ruler you must take decisions with great care and patience. Nothing should be done in a hurry."

Rama did not want bloodshed in the war. He was in favour of making an effort to stop the war by sending a peace mission. He also wanted to make Ravana realize that kidnapping a woman is a sin. So, he should return Sita and avoid useless bloodshed. With this aim, he decided to send Angada whose father was the friend of Ravana as a peace messenger. After receiving the orders of Rama, Angada became ready to meet Ravana.

Having reached the royal court of Ravana, Angada bowed to him and introduced himself. He also told Ravana the purpose of his visit. Hearing the purpose of Angada's visit Ravana became angry and said to him, "You are a big fool. You are favouring the killer of your father, while you are supposed to take revenge. If you are not capable of taking revenge why don't you come to me. I will take your revenge by killing him."

Hearing Ravana, Angada became furious, but did not react because Rama advised him not to loose his temper and have patience under all circumstances.

Thereafter, Angada delivered the message of Rama to Ravana. He said, "Rama does not want bloodshed. Hence, he wants you to return Sita. Otherwise, many innocent people would get killed for nothing. So accept his proposal to avoid the war which is an evil in itself." But Ravana interrupted and said, "Why don't you say that Rama is a coward. He doesn't have

courage to fight with me. Tell him to go back without Sita. I will allow him to return without fight."

At this, Angada lost his temper. In a thunderous voice,

he said, "You will see the power of Rama at the proper time. But first see a glimpse of his servant's powder." Saying this Angada fixed his foot on the ground and said, "Tell your brave men to move my foot." Many of the brave came one by one but failed in their attempt to move his foot. Even Meghnada was not able to move the foot of the Angada.

Having seen this, Ravana started feeling ashamed. He himself descended from the throne to move the foot of Angada. As he bowed down, Angada himself moved his foot aside and said, "There is no need to touch my feet. Go to Rama and touch his feet. It would save you life." Saying so, Angada returned to Rama.

On his return from Lanka, Angada said to Rama, "Oh Lord! I delivered your peace message to Ravana. I also tried to convince him not to fight and return Mata Sita. But he is so intoxicated with his power that he refused."

Rama said, "All right! We have tried our best to avoid bloodshed. But now, we are left with no other alternative except the war."

Thereafter, Lord Rama ordered his army to attack Lanka. After receiving the order of Lord Rama, all the monkeys and bears entered Lanka. They uprooted the trees and threw them on the demons who ran here and there to save their lives. The soldiers

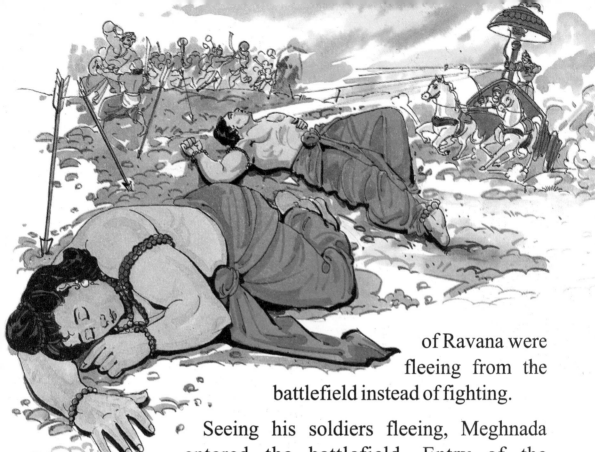

of Ravana were fleeing from the battlefield instead of fighting.

Seeing his soldiers fleeing, Meghnada entered the battlefield. Entry of the Meghnada in the battlefield inspired the demons and they started fighting with a new spirit. Many soldiers died in the battlefield from both the sides. It was a horrible scene where the soldiers were crying in pain. Meghnada, the commander of demons' army and Angada, the leader of Rama's army started fighting with each other. During this fight, Angada broke the chariot of Meghnada. He also killed the charioteer of Meghnada. So Meghnada became helpless.

On the other side, Jambavan, Hanumana and Neela were fighting with the son of Kumbhkarana. Meghnada wanted to finish the war quickly. So, he started using his powers. With the help of these powers he became invisible and attacked Rama and Lakshmana with Nagastra. It made them unconscious. Seeing this, the army of Rama became nervous and uneasy.

On the other hand, thinking Lord Rama and Lakshmana were dead, Meghnada became happy. He passed the news of their victory and Rama and Lakshmana's death in the war to his father, Ravana. After receiving this news, Ravana approached Sita in Ashok Vatika and said, "Sita! You were so confident about the Rama's courage. See my son, Meghnada has killed both Rama and Lakshmana. Now, nobody can save you from me."

But Sita never believed him. She said, "Ravana! Why are you day-dreaming. Nobody in this whole world can kill my Lord Rama."

To make Sita believe him, Ravana took her to the battlefield with Trijata. When Sita saw Rama and Lakshmana in an unconscious state, she started lamenting. Then, Trijata revealed the fact that they were unconscious and consoled her.

Seeing Rama and Lakshmana unconscious, other army commandants like Sugreeva and Hanumana became restless. They were trying to help them regain consciousness. After some time when the effect of the Nagastra reduced, Rama regained consciousness but Lakshmana still did not.

Having seen Lakshmana unconscious, Rama became worried. He asked Hanumana how it all happened. Hanumana said, "My Lord! Meghnada attacked you and Lakshmana with the Nagastra. You have regained consciousness but Lakshmana still hasn't."

At this moment, Garuda, the vehicle of Lord Vishnu appeared there. He rubbed Lakshmana gently with his wings. Lakshmana got up immediately. Rama hugged him with love. When the news of Lakshmana's revival spread in Rama's army, they danced with happiness. When Ravana came to know about the failure of Nagastra, he was surprised. He became very worried and thought, 'Nagastra's failure means that Rama and Lakshmana are not ordinary humans. We must take more precautions. An ordinary person cannot survive the attack of the Nagastra.'

RAVANA JOINS THE WAR

The survival of Rama and Lakshmana increased the worries of Ravana. Then, he decided to send a demon named Dhoomraksh to kill them. But as soon as Dhoomraksh entered the battlefield, Hanumana killed him with his bare hands. When Ravana came to know about it, he decided to fight with them himself.

Seeing Ravana in the battlefield, Hanumana started in his direction. But Lakshmana stopped him on his way. Then, he himself came forward to fight with Ravana. Ravana used a divine weapon against Lakshmana and made him unconscious.

When Rama saw his brother unconscious he showered arrows on Ravana and wounded him. He also destroyed his chariot and weapons. Ravana became helpless.

Seeing Ravana wounded and without chariot, Rama took pity on him. But he knew that it was essential to destroy the magical powers of

demons. And it was possible only after the death of Ravana.
Hence, he decided to kill the demon king, Ravana at all cost.
With this aim in mind, Lord Rama poised an arrow on his bow
and shot it in the direction of Ravana. The arrow pierced the
chest of Ravana. The wound left by Rama's arrow on Ravana's
chest started bleeding profusely. The chariot of Ravana was
already broken. So, Ravana's condition became pitiable.

Seeing such a condition of Ravana, Rama told him to stop the
war. But Ravana faced Lord Rama until the end of the war.

KUMBHKARANA FORCED TO WAKE UP

Having been wounded by Rama, Ravana was sad and disappointed. Moreover, his son Meghnada who was able to conquer Lord Indra was not able to fight long in the war with Rama. Ravana wanted to take revenge of this insult from Rama.

So, Ravana decided to awaken his brother Kumbhkarana. He was a demon who used to sleep for six months due to the curse of the Brahma. Ravana asked his soldiers to awaken Kumbhkarana. Drums were beaten near his ears, but to no effect. Then elephants were made to jump on his body. Besides, many efforts were made to awaken Kumbhkarana. At last, he got up. As soon as he got up, he asked for food because for the last nine months he had been sleeping continuously without taking any food. So the servants immediately served him a lot of meat and wine to satisfy his hunger.

After satisfying his hunger, Kumbhkarana went to Ravana and said in an enquiring tone, "Brother! What could be so urgent that you have woken me up before the scheduled time?" Ravana replied, "Kumbhkarana! Rama, the son of king Dasharatha of Ayodhya has attacked us. A big army of the monkeys and bears is helping them in this war. I want you to destroy Rama and his big army."

Kumbhkarana was a learned person. With the help of his divine sight, he found out everything that had happened until then. Then, he said to Ravana, "I am your younger brother that is why I will follow your orders at any cost. But you have done a wrong thing by going to war with such a great person, Rama. And in the future you will have to pay for that." And saying this, he proceeded to the battlefield.

KUMBHKARANA MEETS HIS END

Despite knowing that Ravana was on the wrong path, his brother Kumbhkarana decided to help him. As Kumbhkarana lived under Ravana's regime, he had no other choice but to follow him.

He went to the battlefield. Seeing such a big demon coming towards them, the monkeys and bears became scared. They started running for their lives. The commanders stopped them with a great difficulty and brought them back. They were trembling with fear. At first Kumbhkarana punched Angada. Having received his punch, Angada became unconscious. Thereafter, Sugreeva came forward to face Kumbhkarana. But, just like Angada, he too fell unconscious on the first attack of Kumbhkarana. Taking Sugreeva with him, Kumbhkarana started for the palace of Ravana. While he was on the way to the palace, Sugreeva regained consciousness. After regaining conscious-

ness, Sugreeva tried to free himself from Kumbhkarana's hold by biting and scratching him on ears, nose and face. Kumbhkarana started crying with pain and threw him away. At that moment, he saw a portion of army surrounded by monkeys. He started killing the monkeys one by one. When Lord Rama saw this, he poised an arrow on his bow and shot it in his direction. It pierced the legs of Kumbhkarana. But still he never desisted from killing the monkeys. So, Lord Rama shot a divine arrow which cut his head off.

With the news of his brother's death, Ravana became sad and Meghnada took a vow to take his revenge from Rama.

Ravana's son Meghnada was a powerful demon who knew all the magical tricks. He already knew that to fight with Rama and Lakshmana was not so easy. So, this time he tried to win the battle by using his magical tricks. He went to the battlefield in his chariot with an image of Sita.

Having reached the battlefield, Meghnada started torturing Sita's image by pulling her hair and throwing her on the ground. The monkeys were upset and worried to see this. Seeing the monkeys sad, Meghnada cut off the head of Sita to make the monkeys nervous. So that they could be killed easily.

LAKSHMANA VERSUS MEGHNADA

Having seen the misdeeds of Meghnada, the monkeys became frightened. They rushed to Rama and narrated the whole incidence to him. They said, "Oh Lord! This time the demon Meghnada brought Mata Sita to the battlefield. At first he tortured her by grabbing her hair and throwing her on the ground. Then, after torturing her he killed her by cutting off her head. After saying so, monkeys started weeping loudly. Rama became very sad. Seeing Rama in such a state, Lakshmana took the pledge to kill Meghnada.

Vibhishana interrupted and said, "Do not worry! Nothing has happened to Sita. It was a magical trick of Meghnada, she is alright." Hearing this, they all breathed a sight of relief.

Next day, Meghnada went to Ravana and said, "I take a pledge that I will kill both Rama and Lakshmana by the end of the day before sunset."

Ravana became very happy to know the plan of his brave son. He collected a big army of demons.

When the army of Rama saw the big army of demons coming towards them, they ran to Rama to inform him about it.

When Lakshmana saw Meghnada with his big army of demons coming towards them, he went to Rama and said, "Brother! The son of Ravana is coming towards us with a big army. Kindly, allow me to fight with him. I want to command my army." Rama said, "Yes! Lakshmana go and come back with victory over demons." Thereafter, Rama ordered Hanumana and Angada to go with Lakshmana for his protection. Both of them accompanied Lakshmana.

After taking the permission of Rama, Lakshmana went to the battlefield to fight with Meghnada. A fierce battle took place between the two. They both were great warriors. When Meghnada realized that he cannot defeat Lakshmana in the fight, he started using magical tricks against him. Seeing this, Lakshmana became furious. In his anger, Lakshmana killed Meghanada's charioteer and broke the chariot. Now, Meghnada thought that his end is near. So, he attacked Lakshmana with Brahmastra.

As the Brahmastra hit Lakshmana, he became unconscious and fell on the ground. The monkeys immediately picked him up and took him out of the battlefield. One of the monkeys rushed to Rama to inform him about the incident.

When Rama heard about the condition of Lakshmana, he became restless. Anyhow, he went to Lakshmana and put his head in his lap. Tears were rolling out of his eyes. He cried, "Oh Lakshmana! Get up and talk to me. Open your eyes and see me!"

Thereafter, he said to Hanumana, "I sent you with Lakshmana to protect him. Then, how did he become unconscious in your presence? Where were you and Angada at that time?"

Rama remained silent for sometime and then again started lamenting, "Dear Lakshmana! Nothing would happen to you. If anything happens to you, how will I face Mata Sumitra? I won't be able to go back to Ayodhya and would kill myself."

Vibhishana consoled Rama and said, "Do not lose your heart. Lakshmana is not so seriously wounded. Call the royal physician Susan from Lanka, he can save Lakshmana."

Hanumana immediately went to Lanka and brought the royal physician Susan with him.

HANUMANA GOES TO THE HIMALAYAS

The royal physician Susan looked at Lakshmana and said, "I have diagnosed Lakshmana's illness and I have come to a conclusion. Lakshmana can recover from the effects of the Brahamshastra but we need Sanjeevani booty (a herbal medicine), an elixir to recover the wounded. It is available only in the Himalayas. If anyone can go to the Himalayas and bring the medicine before sun rise, the life of Lakshmana can be saved."

Hanumana came forward and asked for the details of the herbal medicine, Sanjeevani.

Susan said, "Hanumana! Go to the Himalayas at once. There you will see a tree with four booties (bud-like flowers). Only one is Sanjeevani. It is different from the other three. So, you can recognise it by just looking at it. Bring it here before sunrise. That herb can save the life of Lakshmana."

Hanumana flew away to the Himalayas without wasting any time. He crossed the rivers, hills and forests on his way to the Himalayas. A demon named Kalnemy tried to stop Hanumana

on his way to the Himalayas but Hanumana defeated him. This way Hanumana continued to fly to the Himalayas in search of the Sanjeevani booty.

Soon, Hanumana reached the Himalayas. Though he was able to find the four booties he was unable to recognise the Sanjeevani out of them. So, he picked up the whole hill and flew back to the south. He wanted to reach the spot before sunrise, so that the life of Lakshmana could be saved.

BHARATA ATTACKS HANUMANA

Hanumana was flying back from the Himalayas with the hill of Sanjeevni to the south. He had the hill in his one hand and his club in the other hand. It was dark and the people were sleeping. Bharata was taking a stroll in the royal garden of the palace. When Bharata saw Hanumana passing over Ayodhya with a hill in his hand, he thought, 'It must be some demon flying in the sky with a hill in his hand.'

'In case, he throws the hill on the people of Ayodhya, it would create a havoc in the city.' He was very worried about the safety of the people. So, he decided to save the people of Ayodhya by killing the demon."

With this aim in mind, he hit Hanumana with an arrow. The arrow wounded Hanumana and he fell on the ground but he  never loosened his hold on the hill of Sanjeevani. He cried out in pain, "Oh Rama! Oh Rama!"

Having heard these words from Hanumana, Bharata realised that the creature was not a demon but a devotee of Rama. He rushed to him and asked who he was. Hanumana introduced himself to Bharata and explained the purpose of taking the hill with him. After knowing that

Lakshmana's life was in danger Bharata became worried.

Hanumana consoled him and said, "I am taking the herb Sanjeevani with me. With the help of this booty, Susan will be able to revive Lakshmana. So, there is nothing to worry about." Hanumana asked for the permission of Bharata to leave. After taking his permission, Hanumana proceeded towards Lanka.

Hanumana reached Lanka before sunrise. The physician Susan treated Lakshmana with Sanjeevani. Lakshmana got up and hugged Rama. Seeing Lakshmana alright, all of them were very happy. Lakshmana was surprised by how he came back from the battlefield. Rama told him that Meghnada had shot the Brahamastra at him which made him unconscious. He also told Lakshmana how Hanumana brought the herb, Sanjeevani for him from the Himalayas. At this, Lakshmana became very angry and said, "Where is Meghnada? I will kill him. Today is the last day of his life."

THE END OF MEGHNADA

Lakshmana wanted to take his revenge from Meghnada. So, he started making plans for it. While Lakshmana was making plans, a spy of Vibhishana informed him that Meghnada was performing a yajna to win the war. If it got completed without any obstacle, it would become impossible to win the war. After receiving this information, Lakshmana went to the place with Vibhishana where Meghnada was performing the yajna.

Meghnada was about to complete his yajna when Lakshmana with Hanumana and some other warriors reached there. They disturbed the yajna. Seeing this, Meghnada became angry. He challenged Lakshmana by saying, "Lakshmana! You don't love your life. That is why you come again and again before me. Your brother is already dying of separation from his wife. Now, you want to give another shock to your brother."

Lakshmana said, "Oh! Meghnada! If you are a brave warrior, then get up and fight with me. Do not talk unnecessary things.

Time will tell who will give a shock and to whom. So, pick up your weapons and be ready. You will also come to know whose life is going to end today and whose family members are going to dive into the sea of sorrows."

Having heard Lakshmana's words, Meghnada lost his temper and took out his sword. He went to attack Lakshmana, but this time Lakshmana was very cautious. He not only saved himself from Meghnada's attack but also retaliated it. Thus, a fierce battle ensued between them. Lakshmana threw the Indrastra backed by the holy hymn and cut off the head of Meghnada.

In this way another sinner was killed. Seeing Meghnada dead, gods showered flowers on Lakshmana. They also blessed him. As the news reached the camp of Rama, the army celebrated the victory with great happiness. But in Lanka, people were sad. They were mourning the death of Meghnada.

Having heard about the death of his son Meghnada, Ravana became very sad. He also got terrified as most of the brave demons were killed. He murmured, 'This is going on due to Sita. So, I will kill her.' Thinking this, he took out his sword and proceeded towards Ashok Vatika to kill Sita.

His prime minister Saparshva followed him. When he realised what Ravana was about to do, he stopped him and said, "It does not look good to kill a woman. You are a wise and learned man. If you do so, you and your future generation will get defamed. So, if you want to take revenge of the death of Meghnada, then fight with Rama and defeat him in the war."

The reasoning of his prime minister Saparshva convinced Ravana. He decided to go to the battlefield immediately. He took all his army with him and sat on his chariot. On reaching there, Ravana became very furious.

He started killing the monkeys and bears of Rama's army. Fierce fighting was going on in between Ravana's and Rama's army. A decisive and conclusive war was being fought.

Hanumana, Angada and Sugreeva were shielding their army. They killed Kumbha and Nikumbha, the sons of Kumbhkarana and many other demons like Virupaksha, Vayupraksha and Mahaparshva.

Seeing his soldiers being killed by Ravana, Rama came in front of Ravana and challenged him, "Oh Ravana! Why are you killing the innocents? If you have the guts, fight with me. You are in a habit of showing your power on the weak. You even kidnapped Sita when she was alone and had no one to save her. If I had been there I would have killed you then and there."

Ravana laughed loudly and said, 'It appears that the long separation from Sita and the life of the forest has turned you mad.'

And that is why you are unable to see my ten heads and twenty arms. Do you know that Lord Shiva has made me immortal and nobody can kill me? So, forget Sita and go back to Ayodhya."

Rama and Ravana started fighting. Rama cut the head of Ravana and immediately another head appeared there. Even the divine weapons of Rama became worthless and had no effect on Ravana. Seeing Rama failing again and again in his attempts to kill Ravana, Vibhishana said, "Lord Rama! There is nectar in the navel of Ravana which has made him immortal. So, hit his navel with an arrow to kill him."

Rama shot an arrow at the navel of Ravana. The arrow pierced

his navel and he fell on the ground. On the ground, he uttered the word 'Rama' and then his body became motionless. As the news of Ravana's death reached the camp of Rama, everybody started celebrating their victory. The gods showered flowers on Rama. They were very happy as Rama killed the sinners like Kumbhkarana, Meghnada and Ravana and made earth free of them. The sages, hermits and humans breathed a sigh of relief on realising that now they were free of demons.

Vibhishana knew that Ravana would be killed by Rama. He also knew that his brother is a sinner but even then he wept on the death of his brother. Rama consoled him and the last rites of Ravana were performed.

SITA UNDERGOES A FIRE TEST

After the death of Ravana, Rama sent Hanumana to bring Sita from Ashok Vatika. Hanumana went to Ashok Vatika and bowed to Sita. He told her about the death of Ravana. Then he said, "Mata, I have come here to take you back to Rama."

Having heard these words, Sita became happy. She accompanied Hanumana. When she reached there, tears rolled down from her eyes. Rama also started to weep uncontrollably.

Sita bowed to touch the feet of Rama but Rama stopped her and said, "I know you are as pure as Ganga but you have to undergo a fire-test to prove your fidelity to me. And this you have to perform in front of all the people."

Having heard Rama's words, all the people present there were stunned. They were unable to believe their own ears. Lakshmana drowned in sorrow, as Sita was equal to his mother. Tears rolled down from his eyes but he was helpless. He had to follow the instructions of his elder brother, Rama.

Thereafter, Rama directed Lakshmana to collect some wood

and prepare a fire bed. Then, Rama asked Sita to enter the fire. Sita moved around Rama thrice and then said, "Oh Gods! Accept my greetings. Oh the god of fire! Be a witness of my purity. If I have committed any sin burn me alive."

Saying this, Sita entered the fire. All the people present were surprised to see this. Seeing this, the creator of the world, Lord Brahma asked Rama, "You are Lord Vishnu and Sita is your Lakshmi, then why do you want to test the purity of Sita? You know Sita is as pure as Ganga."

Rama remain silent. Then, the god of fire lifted Sita and handed her over to Rama. Seeing this, all praised Sita.

Then Rama said to Sita, "My Beloved! This test of fire was necessary to show the world that you are pure. After this test nobody would be able to raise a finger on your purity. As for me, I already know how pure and sacred you really are."

Rama made arrangements for the coronation of Vibhishana at the throne of Lanka. He sent Lakshmana, Sugreeva, Angada, Hanumana, Nala, Neela and Jambavan with Vibhishana. The people of Lanka were happy to have a king like Vibhishana.

Then, Vibhishana went to Rama for his blessings. Rama told him to look after the welfare of the people and do justice to all.

The gods were happy as Rama made the world free from demons. So, they went to Rama to express their gratitude and said, "The work for which you have incarnated in the world is now complete. We are thankful to you for this act of kindness. We are obliged to you. Now, tell us what can we do for you in return."

Rama said with folded hands, "I want that the monkeys and bears who have sacrificed their lives for us to regain their lives. I want to see them alive."

Indra said, "As you wish." After saying so, he disappeared. With

the blessings of gods, all the dead monkeys and bears came back to life.

After completing all of the necessary work in Lanka, Rama was eager to return to Ayodhya. His period of his exile was also over. So, he decided to return to Ayodhya without wasting any more time.

Accordingly, Vibhishana made all the arrangements for the return journey to Ayodhya. The Puspak viman was made ready for Rama, Lakshmana and Sita. Vibhishana, Sugreeva and Hanumana also accompanied them in their journey.

When it passed over the sea, Rama showed Sita the bridge over the sea made by Nala and Neela. He also pointed out Kishkindha of Sugreeva. Rama told Sita the whole story.

When the plane reached over the ashram of sage Bharadwaj, Rama expressed his desire to take blessings of the sage. So, the plane landed near the ashram. Rama, Lakshmana, Sita and Hanumana got the blessings of the great sage.

After visiting the ashram of sage Bharadwaj, Rama and all others sat in the Pushpak plane again and proceeded towards the Ayodhya. He was very eager to reach Ayodhya as soon as possible. When the plane landed near Ayodhya, Hanumana rushed to inform Bharata about the return of Rama. The news reached to all corners of Ayodhya. The people celebrated the return of Rama as a great festival. Though it was the day of Amavasya (Night without moon) the citizens lit the earthen lamps of pure ghee to celebrate Rama's return. The palace was decorated like a bride. The whole of the city was illuminated with lights. The people wore new clothes and came on the road to welcome their princes.

Rama met Guru Vashishtha and Vamdev. He bowed to them and took their blessings. Sita, Lakshmana and others also bowed to them and took their blessings. Thereafter, Bharata came and touched the feet of Rama. His eyes were full of tears. Rama hugged him. As they were meeting after a long gap of time, they

became emotional.

Thereafter, Rama, Sita and Lakshmana went to meet the mothers. They bowed to them and touched their feet. The mothers who were waiting for their early return, hugged them all. They were happy to see both their sons and the daughter-in-law Sita. There was happiness all over the palace. The citizens were also eager to see their princes. So, Rama, Lakshmana and Sita went outside and greeted the people. Seeing them, the people became happy and showered flowers on them. They also raised slogans in their praise.

It was decided that the coronation of Rama would take place next day. Rama took bath in the holy water and changed his clothes. Lakshmana and Sita also changed their clothes and wore the royal clothes. Sita was looking like the image of

goddess Lakshmi in jewellery and new clothes.

All preparations were made for the coronation of Rama. Before the coronation, Rama and Sita sought the blessings of the mothers. Thereafter, they went to the royal court. It was full of all types of people. There were special invitations also. Everyone was eager to see the coronation of Rama. After taking the permission of Guru Vashishtha, Rama and Sita sat on the golden throne. Guru Vashishtha put a holy mark on the forehead of Rama and then a diamond crown was placed on his head. The gods showered flowers on Rama from the heaven. Mata Kaushalya, Mata Sumitra and Mata Kaikeyee blessed Rama. Tears of happiness rolled down from their eyes.

After the coronation, a big feast for the people of Ayodhya was organised. Besides, foodgrain and clothes were given to the poor. There was happiness and comfort all over the kingdom.

UTTAR KAND

DEVOTION OF HANUMANA TO RAMA

After the establishment of Rama Rajya in Ayodhya the people became prosperous. They started leading a life full of peace and comfort. Vibhishana, Sugreeva and Hanumana were living there as the guests of king Rama.

After some time, Vibhishana and Sugreeva expressed their desire to return to their respective kingdoms. But Hanumana refused to go back with them and said, "I am a servant and devotee of Rama and have decided to live with him for the rest of my life. I am not going back with you."

Having heard Hanumana, Sugreeva thought that Hanumana wanted to live in luxury, so he said, "You have become habitual of luxuries of life. So, you want to live here." Sugreeva's words hurt Hanumana badly. So, to show his devotion and faith towards Rama he uttered the words "Jai Shri Rama" and tore

out his heart with his nails. All the people present were
surprised to see the image of Rama and Sita in his heart.
Sugreeva realized his mistake and apologised to him. He
praised the devotion and faith of Hanumana for Rama. Then, he
asked for his permission to go to his kingdom. Thereafter, he
went away with Vibhishana.

After his coronation, Rama always thought for the welfare of the people. His administration was meant for the happiness and comforts of the people. He appointed spies to find out the actual feeling of the people about the administration in general and for him in particular. His spies used to mix with the people to know their inner feelings about the rule of Rama. Rama also wanted to know the reaction of the people on the policies and rulings of his administration. He wanted to know if the people are happy with them or if they are agreeing to them because of the fear of administration. Actually, Rama wanted to win the hearts of the people.

On the basis of the reports of his spies, Rama concluded that people were happy and wished to be ruled by him. Nobody was suffering in whole of the city of Ayodhya. They were living in prosperity and enjoying the luxuries of life. He was popular and loved by the people. Hence, he was satisfied with the administration and the policies he adopted for the welfare of his people.

One day, while giving information about Ayodhya and its

people a spy told Rama, "You are very popular as a ruler among the masses. They praise your administration and the bravery with which you have killed the demon Ravana and established peace in the world. But while they praise you as a good ruler they criticise you for your personal life."

Hearing this, Rama became shocked and said, "Why am I being criticised as a man? What is that for which my people criticise me? Tell me immediately."

The spy said, "People believe that Sita is not fit to be called your wife. She lived in the house of Ravana for a long duration of time. So you shouldn't have accepted her again. This would set a bad example for the women of Ayodhya."

Hearing this, Rama became upset. He thought that 'though the purity of Sita was tested in fire, the people are still raising fingers at her. They are also spreading rumours that she has been unfaithful.'

Rama had to bow before the wishes of the people. As a ruler, he had to pay due respect to the feelings of the people. He did not want to ignore the public opinion.

So, he started thinking deeply about the matter.

Rama was very disturbed by the rumours being spread by the people about his personal life. He was also concerned about Sita who was innocent. One day, another spy told Rama, "Maharaj! A washerman was speaking in a satirical language on your personal life."

The spy was feeling a bit uneasy. Rama pacified him and said, "Why are you so worried? Tell me in detail what happened."

The spy said, "Today, while I was passing through a street I heard a washerman who was scolding his wife. I stood by the side of the hut and heard their conversation. The washerman was pushing his wife out of the hut and was saying, "There is no place in my house for you. You have spent last night in someone else's house. I am not Rama who accepted Sita as his wife despite her living with Ravana for a long time. So, get out."

The opinion of the people about him shocked Rama. Though he knew about the chastity of Sita, he was forced to think as a ruler and not as a husband. Every citizen was free to express his opinion about him. The allegations made by the washerman pinched Rama.

Next day, Rama called all his brothers to his room. On receiving the message of Rama his brothers Bharata, Lakshmana and Shatrughna came to him. They greeted Rama and thereafter asked him about the reason of the meeting.

Rama said with heavy heart, "Listen! we belong to the great Raghuvansha dynasty which is shining like a sun and is famous for its justice. I got Sita tested for her chastity on her return from Lanka but still people are not satisfied.

"They are spreading baseless rumours against her because of which our family is getting defamed. So Lakshmana! Take Sita with you on the excuse of pilgrimage and leave her across Ganga near the ashram of sage Valmiki. And don't ask me any questions on this matter. This is an order," he further said.

Having heard the rude words of Rama, Lakshmana became sad and tears started rolling down from his eyes. It was the most difficult job assigned by Rama to Lakshmana so far.

Lakshmana came out of the room of Rama with a heavy heart. He was assigned a duty to take Sita to the forest. Lakshmana went to Sita and bowed to her. "Mata! You have been asking for going on a pilgrimage. Will you like to go

tomorrow with me on a pilgrimage? On hearing this, Sita became happy. She asked Lakshmana in an eager tone, "Yes! I have been longing for such a journey for the last several months. Tell me at what time tomorrow we are going to leave."

"Tomorrow morning, we will leave for the pilgrimage. Keep yourself ready," saying this Lakshmana went away quickly.

Next day, Sita got up early in the morning. She took the blessings of all and sat in the chariot with Lakshmana. Lakshmana drove away the chariot quickly. He wanted to cross the border of Ayodhya as soon as possible.

Having reached the bank of Ganga, Lakshmana stopped the chariot. He was unable to tell the truth to Sita. At last, he fell at

the feet of Sita and said, "Oh Mata! Please, pardon me. I told you a lie that I am taking you on a pilgrimage. Brother Rama has decided to abandon you. He had to take this decision because the people of Ayodhya don't have a good opinion about you. I came to leave you here. There is a ashram of sage Valmiki nearby. You can live there. Kindly pardon me for this cruel act and allow me to go," after saying Lakshmana started weeping.

When Sita heard that she was being abandoned by Rama, she fell on the ground and became unconscious. After some time, she regained her consciousness and said, "Lakshmana! Have I come on this earth to suffer only? I am being punished for the act which I have never committed. Is this the justice in Rama Rajya? You can go now. Since, you are obeying the order of you brother. I have forgiven you. I would have committed suicide, had I not bore the successor of Raghuvansha. Go now, my blessings are with you."

Lakshmana went thrice around Sita and then touched her feet. Thereafter, he returned to Ayodhya, leaving Sita there. Sita sat on the ground and started weeping.

SITA AT THE ASHRAM

After the departure of Lakshmana, Sita sat there and wept for a long time. After some time, some pupils of Valmiki passed by. When they saw Sita sitting there, they ran to inform Valmiki. They said to him, "Guruji! A woman is sitting at the bank of Ganga. She is crying loudly. It appears that she belongs to a royal family."

Having heard these words, Valmiki smiled. He found out everything about Sita with the help of his divine power. He went to the bank of Ganga with his pupil. On reaching there, he said, "Oh Janaknandini! Do not weep. One has to bear whatever is written in fate. You are welcome in my ashram. Live with comforts along with other women. They will take care of you. I know everything that has happened until now. I also know what would happen in the future. I know you are pure and innocent. You are like my daughter. So, come with me to your new house." Though Sita was very sad because of her abandonment by Rama, the soothing words of Valmiki and his affection consoled her. She went with him to his ashram and started living with other women of the ashram.

LAVA AND KUSHA ARE BORN

After several months, Sita gave birth to two identical twins in the ashram of sage Valmiki. One of the Sadhvis informed Valmiki about the birth of two sons.

Valmiki was very happy to hear about the birth of two sons to Sita. He left immediately for the hut of Sita. He took some Kusha grass with him and reached the hut chanting some holy verses. He gave the Kusha grass to the maid who was serving Sita and said, "Clean the child who came first to this world by the upper portion of the grass and clean next by the lower portion of the grass. The first will be named as Kusha and the second will be called Lava."

The maid followed the instructions of Valmiki. This way the two sons of Sita were named as Lava and Kusha. Their birthday was celebrated with great pomp and show in the ashram.

Gradually, Lava-Kusha started growing under the care of Sita and sage Valmiki. Valmiki taught them vedas, shastras, etc. He also taught them the art of archery. Lava and Kusha became expert in all the fields. Valmiki also told them about his book on Rama and Sita and made them learn it by heart. Several years passed like this.

RAMA ORGANISES ASHVAMEDHA YAJNA

Rama wanted to extend the boundary of his kingdom. So, he decided to perform the Ashvamedha yajna. He sent invitations to all the kings and sages. Many persons came there like Kuber, Varshan, Nala, Neela, Vibhishana, Sugreeva and Jambavan.

As Sita was not there her golden statue was put besides Rama on the throne. The yajna started on the bank of the Gomti with the chanting of holy verses. Rama offered oblation to the sacrificial fire. On the instructions of Rama, precious diamond, silver and gold gifts were given to the guests and the poor.

Thereafter, a well decorated horse of white colour was brought to the sacrificial place. Rama put a holy mark on the forehead of the horse. A golden plate was tied on the neck of the horse. On it, these words were written—'This horse belongs to Rama, the king of Kaushal. Whosoever dares to catch the horse has to fight with Rama or accept his the supremacy.'

The horse of Ashvamedha was released from the Yajnashala. Shatrughna was following the horse with a big army. Rama had

issued clear instructions not to tease or terrorise the poor or weak on the way. The horse passed through different territories and the kings accepted supremacy of Rama over them. They also paid taxes.

This way, the horse passed through different states without any obstacle. At last, it entered a forest and reached the ashram of Valmiki. When Lava and Kusha saw the well decorated horse roaming around they caught it. Then, they tied the horse to a tree. They read the plate and became ready to fight with the army. So, they sat on a stone near the horse and started waiting for them to arrive.

Shatrughna, the brother of Rama was following the horse. When he reached there, he was surprised to see the horse tied to a tree and the two young boys sitting near the horse. He concluded that the horse was caught by these boys. So, he said to them with great affection, "Hello, dear children! The horse is not meant for playing. So leave it." But Lava and Kusha refused and said, "You look like a king. A king should not make a request. Are you afraid of fighting us?" Hearing this, Shatrughna became angry and poised an arrow on his bow. Then he shot it aiming the children, but it failed. Then, both the brothers showered a large numbers of arrows on him and destroyed his chariot. His soldiers were unable to catch them. One of the arrows made Shatrughna unconscious. Seeing Shatrughna unconscious his army fled from the battlefield.

The soldiers went back to Rama and narrated the whole of the incident to him. Then, Rama sent Lakshmana with another army to look into the matter and get the horse released.

LAKSHMANA VERSUS LAVA-KUSHA

Lakshmana reached the battlefield with his army. But when he saw the two boys in the battlefield, he became emotional and poured affection on them. He pleaded with them to release the horse. But they refused and showered arrows on him. They cut the crown of Lakshmana as well.

In exchange, Lakshmana also shot arrows at them but nothing happened. Then, Lakshmana used some divine weapons on them to make them unconscious but they also proved ineffective on them. Then, he threw an arrow in the name of Rama which made Kusha unconscious. But when Lava prayed to Valmiki, Kusha again regained consciousness. Then Lava threw invisible arrows of Valmiki on Lakshmana. It made him unconscious. Seeing this, the army of Lakshmana also fled from the battlefield. This way, the two brothers Lava and Kusha defeated the whole army of both Shatrughna and Lakshmana.

BHARATA VERSUS LAVA-KUSHA

When Rama received the news of Lakshmana's defeat, he went to Bharata and asked him to fight with the boys. He said to him, "The two pupils of Valmiki are not ordinary human beings. They have defeated Lakshmana and Shatrughna. They have also killed a large number our many soldiers. So, fight with them with great care."

After hearing Rama, Bharata went to Hanumana and said, "The two pupils of Valmiki had caught the horse of Ashvamedha. So, come with me along with Jambavan, Sugreeva, Angada, Nala and Neela. Hanumana accompanied Bharata with his army. Seeing the army of Hanumana coming towards them, both the boys got ready. They killed several soldiers of Hanumana. Hanumana was feeling happy to see such brave boys but Bharata was angry with them.

In a fit of anger, Bharata shot an arrow towards Lava and made him unconscious. Seeing his brother unconscious, Kusha shot an arrow towards Bharata which made him unconscious.

Seeing such a display of courage, Hanumana realised that these boys cannot be an ordinary human beings. So, he used

his divine sight to find out their background and soon realised that these boys are actually the sons of Rama and Sita.

When the news of the defeat of Bharata reached Rama, he decided to go to the battlefield.

He reached there and asked the boys. "Who are you? Would you tell me the name of your parents? You have already shown your bravery and courage by defeating my brothers and army."

Hearing Rama, Lava and Kusha said, "You want to misguide us by your sweet talk. We want to fight you."

Rama said, "Before the fight, I want to know about your background. Tell me who are your parents. Introduce yourself."

Hearing Rama, both the brothers said, "We are the sons of Sita who is the daughter of Mithila king, Janaka. We received our education in the ashram of sage Valmiki. He has taught us many things but we don't know who is our father."

Saying this, both the boys looked to Rama to fight.

When Rama realised that both Lava and Kusha are his own sons, he became very happy. But both of them were challenging Rama to fight. So, he picked up his bow and poised an arrow unwillingly. However, he was not able to fight against his own sons. Seeing Rama nervous, both of them wondered why the killer of the big demons like Ravana and Kumbhkarana was not responding to their open challenge to fight.

But Hanumana who was seeing all this, understood the dilemma of Rama. He picked up his club and attacked Lava and Kusha. In retaliation Kusha started hand to hand bout with Hanumana. He defeated Hanumana in the bout and tied him up with a rope.

Thereafter, both the boys took Hanumana to their mother. On reaching, they called their mother, "See Matashri! We have brought this monkey from the battlefield. We defeated him in the battle."

Having heard their son's words, Sita came out of her hut. She was surprised to see Hanumana tied with a rope.

RAMA MEETS LAVA-KUSHA

Seeing Sita, Hanumana became very happy. He bowed to her and said, "Mata! You are great that you have given birth to these brave children. They have defeated Bharata, Shatrughna and Lakshmana and killed many soldiers of their army. Now, they are going to fight with Lord Rama himself."

Sita was shocked when she heard this. She asked her sons to release Hanumana immediately. Her sons obeyed the order of their mother. Then, Sita went to Valmiki and said, "Oh Great Sage! What am I hearing? Are my sons going to fight with their father now? Is it true that my sons are going to defame the great Raghuvansha dynasty by fighting with their father and uncle?"

Seeing Sita in such a distressed mood, Valmiki tried to pacify her. He said, "Do not worry. I will go to the battlefield tomorrow and try to bring the situation under control."

Sita went back to her hut on the assurance of Valmiki.

Next day, Valmiki reached the battlefield. There, he saw Lava and Kusha challenging their father, Rama for a fight. In answer to their challenge Rama said, "Go back to your home children! You should be playing instead of fighting."

Lava-Kusha did not like it. They thought that Rama is making fun of them. So, they insisted on fighting. Rama tried to make

them understand but the children remained stuck to their demand. At last, Rama bowed to their demands and became ready to shoot an invisible arrow. Before he could do that, sage Valmiki came there and stopped him. Seeing the sage, Rama put the bow aside and bowed to him.

Valmiki told him, "Rama! These are your children. Their mother is Sita. The name of your elder son is Kusha and the younger is Lava. When Lakshmana left Sita on the bank of Ganga, she was pregnant at that time. The sons were born in my ashram. They were brought up under my supervision. I taught them many acts and weaponry and gave them divine weapons."

Rama became happy when he heard this. He came forward and hugged them. Valmiki asked the children to touch the feet of Rama and take his blessings. Then, Valmiki brought Bharata, Lakshmana and Shatrughna back to consciousness. They touched the feet of Valmiki and took his blessings. He also revived the rest of the soldiers killed by Lava and Kusha. Everybody was happy to meet the sons of Rama.

At this moment, Sita reached the battlefield. Having seen her, all became very happy. Lakshmana, Shatrughna and Bharata bowed to Sita. But Rama was still silent and thinking of the people's taunting on his personal life. So, Sita became very sad.

Sage Valmiki said to Sita, "Now your days of sufferings and sorrows are over. Now return to Ayodhya and lead a happy life." Sita also wanted to go back. So, she started looking towards Rama with eyes full of hope and expectation. She was waiting for Rama to ask her to go to Ayodhya.

Valmiki guessed the seriousness of the situation and said to Rama, "Oh great King Rama! Sita is as sacred as Ganga. I have seen through my divine sight that there is none except you in her heart. So, accept her without hesitation."

Hearing Valmiki, Rama said nothing but he instructed Lakshmana to take Sita back to Ayodhya. Lakshmana said to Sita, "One day I left you in the forest. Now, I am asking you to come to Ayodhya with us."

Hearing Lakshmana, Sita said, "Lakshmana! How can I go back to Ayodhya? The man who abandoned me is not asking me to return to Ayodhya. I can go back only if the father of my

children asks me to return to Ayodhya."

Seeing Lakshmana failing in his attempt to bring Sita back to Ayodhya, Bharata and Shatrughna also started requesting Sita to come back home. But she refused to go. She was unable to bear the rude and cruel behaviour of Rama. So, she went to the bank of Saryu river and said to Mother Earth in a loud voice, "I am a faithful wife. I have only Rama in my mind. If I have only Rama in my heart and soul, then take me in your lap." As soon as Sita uttered these words, a big jolt shook the earth and it became divided into two parts. From this crack, Goddess Earth came out. She took Sita in her lap and disappeared into the earth. When Lava and Kusha saw their mother getting sucked up in the earth they started weeping. Rama cried in anger, "O Mother Earth! Return my Sita or I will burn the whole of the universe."

At this, Brahma appeared and pacified Rama, "Do not worry. You will meet Sita soon in the heaven." So Rama decided to go back to Ayodhya with a heavy heart.

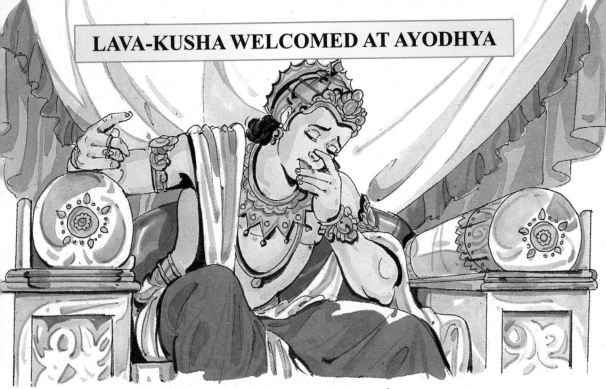

In Ayodhya, everybody knew about the two courageous children who caught the horse of Ashwamedha yajna. When it came to their knowledge that Lava and Kusha were actually the sons of Rama, they became eager to see them. The palace was decorated for their welcome. The people were standing in lines for a glimpse of their princes.

People decorated their houses and lit earthen lamps.

When Chakravarti Emperor Rama reached Ayodhya with Lava and Kusha, people came out of their houses to see them. A warm welcome was given to them in the palace. Rajmata Kaushalya, Queen Sumitra and Kaikeyee blessed them.

Time passed gradually. There was prosperity and peace in Ayodhya. Only Rama was sad in the absence of Sita.

With the passage of time, all the three mothers also died. Thereafter, Rama started feeling lonely. It was very difficult for him to live alone.

One day, while thinking about his rule and work he had done for the people, he started calculating the time he had passed on the earth. On calculation, he found that he had ruled over eleven thousand years on the earth and all the assignments for which he had incarnated on earth were finished by then. So, he decided to go to Vishnudham where his wife, Sita would be waiting for him.

On the other side, Vishnu was also thinking about the return of Rama to Vishnudham. He was thinking that Rama had completed his tasks as a man and a ruler. So, it was time for him to come back to Vishnudham. Keeping this in mind he asked the sage Narada to call Dharmraj (The god of death).

Having received Vishnu's order, Dharmraj reached Vishnudham. He bowed to Vishnu and said, "O Lord! What can I do for you?" Vishnu said, "You know, Rama was incarnated on earth for some special purposes. Now as all those purposes are solved, bring him back to Vishnudham with respect."

Hearing Vishnu, Dharmraj said, "As you wish." Having said this, Dharmraj proceeded to the earth to take Rama.

It was very easy for Dharmraj to take an ordinary human to Yam Lok on the completion of their age. But this time it was very difficult task as he had to take Shri Rama with him who was the incarnation of Lord Vishnu. He was thinking of the way by which he could do that.

Dharmraj entered Ayodhya in the disguise of a brahmin (priest). But he was unable to decide how to enter the palace. The biggest problem was that how he would introduce himself to Rama. How will he say to Rama that his time on the earth was up and he has come here to take him to Vishnudham?

Thinking all this, he reached the palace. As he was about to open the main gate, Rama himself came out to receive him. After the conventional welcome of Dharmraj, Rama took him to his personal room and asked him to sit there. Thereafter, he said to Lakshmana, "Do not allow anyone to enter my room. I am discussing a very important matter right now. It's an order."

On the instructions of Rama, Lakshmana stood as a guard at the gate of the Rama's personal room.

When they were alone, Dharmraj introduced himself to Rama

and disclosed the purpose of his visit. Rama replied with patience, "I have completed all my works on the earth. So, I was waiting for you to take me to the Vishnudham. Kindly, take me there with you as soon as possible.

Rama talked to Dharmraj boldly without any fear. He was not afraid of death because he knew that death cannot kill the soul. Soul is immortal. Unlike the body, it is imperishable.

When Rama was discussing it with Dharmraj, Lakshmana was guarding the room. At this moment, sage Durvasa came there and said, "Lakshmana, go and inform Rama about my arrival."

Lakshmana replied humbly, "Sorry Great Sage! Rama is consulting an important matter with a brahmin right now and nobody is allowed to enter his room. So, please wait for some time. As soon as the consultation gets finished, I will inform Rama about you."

Having heard Lakshmana's words, the sage Durvasa became angry and in a thunderous voice he said, "Inform Rama immediately about my arrival. Otherwise, I will finish all of

your clan as well as whole of the state."

Lakshmana thought, 'If I do not obey the sage Durvasa's orders, he will finish our family and state. So it would be better to accept his order and inform Rama. Thinking this, Lakshmana entered the room of Rama. The latter was very surprised to see Lakshmana in the room despite his instruction not to come. Anyhow, Lakshmana informed Rama of the sage's arrival. Then, Rama went outside and bowed to the sage. He brought him inside and served him breakfast. Then, he requested the sage not to disclose his talks with Dharmraj.

Lakshmana was very sad that he had disobeyed the orders of Rama for the first time. So, he said to Lord Rama, "Brother! Today, I have disobeyed your orders. So, I have no right to live on the earth. Now permit me to go from the earth."

Having got the permission of Rama, Lakshmana went to the river Saryu. Then he collected all his senses and his soul left his body. Indra came from the heaven to take Lakshmana on his chariot. Thus, Lakshmana went with Indra to heaven.

After the departure of Lakshmana, Rama became lonely. He was no more interested in living on the earth and wanted to meet his relatives in heaven. He consulted his courtiers and made Lava and Kusha the king of South and North Kaushal respectively. Then, he asked Bharata to rule over Ayodhya. He said, "Bharata, take care of the people of Ayodhya. My time on the earth is up. Now, I want to go to the heaven."

Hearing Rama, Bharata started weeping. After controlling himself a little bit, he said, "Without you, Shatrughna and I won't be able to live any long. So, please take us also with you."

At this moment, Vashishtha also reached there and said, "Do not worry about the future. The people of Ayodhya have come to know that Rama is going to the heaven. So, they all are ready to go with you."

Hearing Vashishtha, Rama peeped out of his palace. On seeing Rama all cried in the same tone, "Oh Rama! We will all go with you. We cannot live here without you."

Seeing the people of Ayodhya looking towards him with such hope, Rama agreed to take them with him. Then, he thought to say goodbye to all his relatives and brothers.

RAMA BIDS GOODBYE

Soon, the news of the departure of Rama reached Lanka. Hearing this, Vibhishana immediately reached Ayodhya to meet Rama. He bowed to Rama. While giving his blessings Rama said to him, "Vibhishana! You will rule over Lanka for years. Always be a kind and just king. Take care of the people and worship Lord Vishnu."

Then, Rama said, "Hanumana, I know that you want to live as my true devotee. My blessings are with you. Live here till my name prevails on the earth. You will be known with my name."

Hanumana became very happy because the blessings of Rama had made him immortal. He knew that the name of Rama and his stories will exist on the earth for ever. And he would serve his lord by singing songs in his praise for the years to come. It is seen that on hearing the Ramayana or by singing the songs of the Ramayana people get relieved from their worries. Besides this, the poor get wealth and the issueless people get children. There is nothing which cannot be achieved by chanting Rama-Rama. So, read Ramayana and try to follow the principles of Rama in your life.

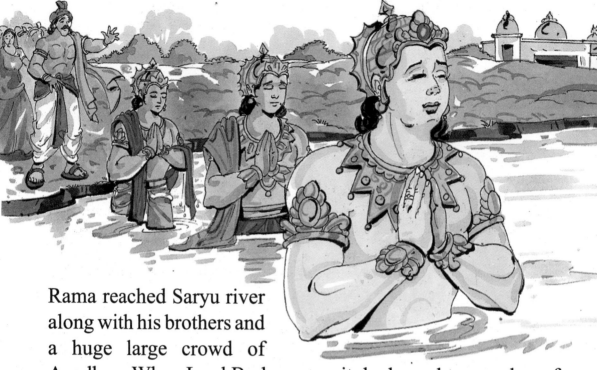

Rama reached Saryu river along with his brothers and a huge large crowd of Ayodhya. When Lord Brahma saw it, he brought a number of golden chariots with him in the sky. He spoke in a loud voice. "O incarnation of Vishnu! Come to heaven on any chariot of your choice."

As soon as Rama, Bharata and Shatrughna entered the river Saryu, they immediately got mingled with Vishnu. Then, Rama said to Brahma, "Oh Lord, allow all of my devotees who are following me.

Hence, all the people, monkeys, bears, etc. who were following Rama got to heaven. Not only this, the birds sitting on the tree near Saryu also got to heaven. To the surprise of all, even the sinners who were living near Saryu river also went to heaven.

The name of Rama, Ayodhya and Saryu river are still believed to be the gateway to heaven.

PRAISE OF RAMA BY HANUMANA

The devotee of Rama, Hanumana turned immortal by the blessings of Rama. After the departure of Rama to heaven, Hanumana kept himself busy in spreading the Rama-Katha (story of Rama) all over the earth. It is believed that wherever Rama Katha is heard or Lord Rama is worshipped, Hanumana

reaches there. Since Hanumana is the devotee of Rama, he fulfills the desires of those who utter the name of Rama or worship him. Hanumana takes care of the people who worship Rama.

Ramayana has become a medicine which saves the humans from the circle of birth and rebirth. The reading and hearing of Ramayana makes the people happy and prosperous.

In the present age of Kali, Ramayana makes the people free of sins. So, we should never forget the name of Rama. We should chant 'Rama' daily. We should also remember that the protagonists of *Ramayana*—Rama, Lakshmana, Bharata and Shatrughna were ideal sons as well as ideal brothers. Similarly, Sita was an ideal wife. Hanumana was a true devotee of Lord Rama.

Therefore, we must follow the ideals of Rama, *Ramayana* and Hanumana in our life. This is the only way of salvation for us.